User's Guide
to Powder Coating

Fourth Edition

User's Guide to Powder Coating

Fourth Edition

Nicholas Liberto

Editor

Society of
Manufacturing
Engineers
www.sme.org

Association
for Finishing
Processes/SME
www.sme.org/afp

Dearborn, Michigan

Library of Congress Catalog Card Number: 2002117253
International Standard Book Number: 0-87263-648-8

Additional copies may be obtained by contacting:
Society of Manufacturing Engineers
Customer Service
One SME Drive, P.O. Box 930
Dearborn, Michigan 48121
1-800-733-4763
www.sme.org

SME staff who participated in producing this book:
Cheryl Zupan, Staff Editor
Rosemary Csizmadia, Production Supervisor
Frances Kania, Production Assistant
Kathye Quirk, Graphic Designer/Cover Design
Jon Newberg, Production Editor

Printed in the United States of America

About the Society of Manufacturing Engineers (SME)

The Society of Manufacturing Engineers is the world's leading professional society supporting manufacturing education. Through its member programs, publications, expositions, and professional development resources, SME promotes an increased awareness of manufacturing engineering and helps keep manufacturing professionals up to date on leading trends and technologies. Headquartered in Michigan, SME influences more than half a million manufacturing engineers and executives annually. The Society has members in 70 countries and is supported by a network of hundreds of chapters worldwide. Visit SME at www.sme.org.

About AFP/SME

The Association for Finishing Processes of SME (AFP/SME) covers all technology, process, and management aspects of cleaning and coating metal and plastic parts used in manufactured products. Members are in the big automotive and aerospace plants and Tier One supplier facilities, as well as in companies manufacturing everything from office furniture to toys. AFP/SME members include process engineers who implement automated powder coating lines; product engineers who specify liquid, waterborne, or electrostatic finishes; managers of processes such as deburring, buffing, polishing, or chemical pretreatment; and supervisors of post-production air and water treatment, emissions control, recycling, and liquid waste and sludge disposal systems. AFP/SME sponsors national conferences and regional clinics on topics such as planning painting system layouts, troubleshooting coating durability problems and defects, evaluating advanced curing technologies, decorating plastics, implementing robotic finishing lines, and analyzing EPA regulations. To find out more, visit AFP/SME at www.sme.org/afp.

Table of Contents

Preface

Powder coating use hit the North American market in the late 1960s. Its usage has continued to grow since that time. Offering superior appearance, mechanical-, corrosion-, and solvent-resistance properties, powder coating use has taken the finishing market by storm. In the early days of this technology, potential end users first had to be educated about the powder coating process. Companies today that "paint" their products always ask about powder as an alternative to using a liquid coating. This acceptance of powder coating did not happen overnight, however. It took more than 30 years for suppliers and organizations like SME to educate the marketplace on the benefits of this technology.

As a result of increased awareness, powder coating is being used on more and more products, including products that just recently were considered impractical for powder coating. For instance, high-temperature applications where the product may reach temperatures of up to 1,000° F (538° C) are routinely powder coated today. Conversely, many temperature-sensitive substrates like plastic and wood products are now powder coated with UV-curable materials. Only a few years ago both high temperature products and temperature-sensitive substrates were considered impossible to powder coat.

As always, powder coating is a low-cost, high-performance finish. The process is environmentally friendly. Similar attributes are not available with any other organic coating technology, at least not in one package. Such attributes are the main reason for the tremendous growth and acceptance of this technology.

Along with improvements in the industry, equipment suppliers have developed improved systems to deal with the nagging difficulties of employing a new powder coating process. Achieving faster color change, increasing transfer efficiency, and reducing overall powder usage are a few examples of recent improvements. Today there are even inexpensive systems available for the hobbyist or home user of powder coating.

This book has been updated to reflect recent technological improvements to powder coating. Now in its fourth edition, the *Users Guide to Powder Coating* has become the mainstay reference for novice and expert alike. I am proud to have been a current and past contributing author and selected to be the current editor of this manuscript. It is hoped that you continue to find this book useful in your powder coating activities.

Nicholas Liberto, Editor

one

Why Powder Coating?

The use of powder coating as a finishing process has grown significantly in the past several years. More and more companies have turned to powder coating as a way to produce a high-quality finish while increasing production rates, cutting costs, and complying with increasing environmental pressures. Also, ongoing technological breakthroughs are continually knocking down the few barriers that hindered powder coating's ability to grow in the market. In fact, powder coating now constitutes 20% of the finishing market where it competes directly with traditional liquid finishes. It covers over 15% of the total industrial finishing market in North America.

With recent and pending environmental regulations on air and water emissions and waste disposal, the switch from liquid to powder finishing is becoming more prevalent. Liquid finishing requires the use of solvents to convey the resinous binder over a surface. These liquid solvents necessitate venting, filtering, and solvent recovery systems to control volatile organic compounds (VOC). Powder coating, on the other hand, is a dry finish, which does not use VOC during any part of the finishing operation.

In powder coating, the finely ground particles of pigment and resin are electrostatically charged and sprayed onto a metal part. The coating process can be done manually or automatically with a wide variety of equipment available to small and large end users. The parts to be coated are neutrally grounded. The charged particles projected at them adhere to the parts and are held there until melted and fused into a smooth coating in the curing ovens. The result is a uniform, durable, high-quality finish.

ECONOMIC CONSIDERATIONS

The excellence of the powder-coated finish when compared to liquid coating systems is accompanied by substantial cost savings. Since powder contains no VOC, air used to exhaust the powder spray booth can be recirculated directly to the plant, eliminating the cost of heating or cooling the makeup air. Ovens that cure solvent-based coatings must heat and exhaust huge volumes of air to ensure that the solvent fumes do not reach a potentially explosive level. With no solvent in powder coating, the exhaust required in the ovens is lower, resulting in energy and cost savings in spite of the higher curing temperatures powder coating requires.

Labor and Efficiency Savings

There are savings in labor costs because less training is required to operate a powder coating system. There is no mixing of powder with solvents or catalysts. Maintenance costs are also low, as most clean-ups can be done with a vacuum.

The powder application system can bring greater operating efficiency to the finishing operation, which can save time and money. Parts can be racked closer together on a conveyor, so more parts can pass through a production line in a given period of time, resulting in lower unit costs. More parts can be coated automatically, as powder coating does not run, drip, or sag, consequently resulting in significantly lower reject rates. With appropriate application equipment, powder materials, and efficient recovery methods, one-coat application and overall powder utilization efficiency of 95–98% is readily achievable. If more than one color is required, color change can be accomplished in a relatively short period of time. And up to 99% of the powder sprayed at the product surface, but not adhering, can be recovered and reused, resulting in minimal waste disposal costs.

Today's powder coatings offer wide ranges of performance properties and glosses, and they can match virtually any color or texture. Film thicknesses from under 1 mil (0.03 mm) to over 15 mil (0.38 mm) are possible.

APPLICATIONS

Powder coatings are now used in hundreds of applications. As market potential grows, research devoted to product improvement also increases, leading to further innovations and market expansion.

Powder Coating Markets

One of the biggest powder-coating users is the appliance industry. The high-quality finish is both attractive and durable, and a viable alternative for porcelain enamel and liquid finishes on traditional appliance surfaces. These include dryer drums, front and side panels of ranges and refrigerators, washer tops and lids, air conditioner cabinets, water heaters, dishwasher racks, and cavities of microwave ovens. Technological developments have resulted in powder coatings with lower gloss, lower-temperature-curing requirements, and stronger resistance to chips, scratches, detergents, and grease. All these features have led to the use of powder coatings on about 40% of all appliance finishes. Appliance applications represent about 21% of the North American powder coating market.

The automotive industry represents approximately an additional 15% of the North American powder coating market. Wheels, bumpers, roof racks, door handles, interior panels, and various "under-the-hood" parts are being powder coated. Powder is also used as a primer-surfacer on component parts for trucks and recreational vehicles. Clear powders, over a liquid base coat, are being developed for exterior auto body finishing. While only three manufacturers use clear powders in limited models, it is still hoped that their use is mainstreamed in the future.

The architectural and building market uses powder coating on file cabinets, shelving, aluminum extrusions for window frames, door frames, and modular office furniture. Posts, rails, fencing, metal gutters, highway and parking lot poles, guardrails, farm implements, garden tools and tractors, patio furniture, and other products used outdoors all benefit from the high weatherability properties of powder coating.

Countless everyday uses for powder coating include fire extinguishers, mechanical pencils and pens, thumbtacks, barbecue grills, and vending machines. Sporting goods equipment uses include bicycle frames, golf-club shafts, ski poles, and exercise equipment. Technological advancements have allowed expansion of powder coating to nonmetal surfaces, such as ceramics, wood, plastic, and brass, so that bottles, shower stalls, dashboards, and even wooden office furniture components are now powder coated.

ENVIRONMENTAL IMPLICATIONS

With the current emphasis on control of emissions from industrial processes and overall concerns about air quality, ground water, and hazardous wastes, powder coatings offer an environmental advantage that may be a determining factor in selecting powder coating as a finishing process.

No solvents are involved in the mixing, application, or clean up of a powder coating operation, virtually eliminating solvent emissions and the need for venting, filtering, or solvent recovery systems that would be required to control VOC. This greatly simplifies the permitting process needed for installation, expansion, and operation of facilities, and makes compliance with federal and state regulations much easier. It also allows the possibility of including a finishing operation in a non-attainment area where other systems may not be permitted.

Non-hazardous Powders

Powders used for powder coatings are solids and most are classified as nonhazardous. Their use eliminates or minimizes problems and expenses associated with disposal of hazardous wastes from a finishing process. There is no sludge, fouled spray booth filters, or solvent to contend with. Up to 99% of powder overspray can be recovered and reused. Automatic recycling units collect the overspray powder and return it directly to the feed hopper, where it returns to the system. In instances where there is waste, it can be handled as a non-water-soluble solid, presenting few disposal problems.

POWDER COATING GROWTH

Because of their advantages over liquid systems, powder coating system installations continue at a dramatic rate. Development work on materials, equipment, and new applications and surfaces will bring dynamic changes to the powder coating industry. Applications not possible a few years ago may become practical and advantageous in the near future. The potential powder user should work closely with suppliers to stay current on the latest developments in powder coating materials, application, maintenance, and clean up. With continually changing environmental regulations, it is best to check with local officials for disposal recommendations.

The use of powder coating as a finishing process has grown rapidly, with no signs of slowing down anytime soon. This manual will assist you in understanding the process, materials, and application methods of this ever-growing finishing technology.

two

Powder Coating Materials

Powder coating, a unique class of coating material produced and used in powder form, is renowned among present-day compliance coatings. Dry, solid, and film-forming coating powders are distinguished from liquid materials used in high-solids, water-reducible, radiation-cure, and electro-coat technologies.

Powder coating is not in fact, a protective, decorative paint until a coated item emerges from the hot-oven cycle, which is necessary to complete curing or fusion. Prior to baking, coating powders are finely ground plastic compositions. Consequently, most resins used in powder coatings are quite different from those used with liquid paints. Liquid paints require resins that are soluble or miscible with solvents and/or water, while powder coatings require resins that are solid. Powder-coating resins must be solid at ambient and reasonably elevated storage temperatures. They also must be capable of melting sharply to a low-viscosity index to permit flow to a continuous-coating film when heated.

In the early years of powder, the 1960s and 70s, the number of solid-resin systems available for the manufacture of coating powders was relatively restricted. Consequently, there were limitations on the industry's ability to meet the diverse needs of the finishing industry. However, growth of the powder-coating industry has been accompanied by technological expansion resulting in many new resin systems and other functional components. This has made a wider range of coating powders available to meet and often beat the properties of most of today's solvent- or water-based baking enamels.

Three major types of coating powders are available to industrial finishers: thermoplastic, thermoset, and radiation cured. Like other industrial surface coatings, coating powders are individually formulated to meet very specific finishing needs as defined by the end user. This includes matching the finisher's desired color and appearance and film-performance requirements, all within particular restrictions on the finishers coating operation. New powders with unique properties are constantly emerging. Accordingly, as with the selection of any industrial finish, a close relationship must be developed between users and suppliers of powder. This allows exacting requirements to be thoroughly understood and the correct finishing powder to be supplied.

As the powder-coating industry continues to mature, many powder formulators have expanded their standard products to include a wide variety of ready-to-use formulations. This has allowed end users the option of selecting a powder from stock for quick delivery at a lower cost. Whether selecting a stock material or a custom formulation, the end user is encouraged to select a coating based on detailed specifications that enumerate all pertinent physical and appearance properties required in the end use of a coating.

THERMOPLASTIC POWDERS

Upon application of heat, thermoplastic powder melts and flows to form a film. It continues to have the same chemical composition when it solidifies again upon cooling. Thermoplastic coating powders are based on thermoplastic resins of high-molecular weight. Flow and film properties of these coatings depend on the basic properties of the resins. These tough, resilient, and more costly resins tend to present difficulties when ground into the very fine particles necessary for spray application and fusing of thin films. Consequently, thermoplastic resin systems are used more commonly as functional coatings at higher-film thicknesses. They are commonly applied with the fluidized-bed-application technique by preheating the metal above the melt temperature of the polymer. Thermoplastic powders are most suitable for coating items requiring a thicker film for extreme performance. They do not generally compete in the same markets as liquid paints.

Polyethylene

Polyethylene powders were the first thermoplastic coating powders offered to industry. They have excellent chemical resistance, toughness, and electrical-insulation properties. The film surface of such coatings is smooth, warm to the touch, and of medium gloss. Polyethylene coatings have good release properties, allowing viscous, sticky materials to be cleaned from their surfaces. High-density polyethylene coatings are tougher and more chemically resistant than low-density coatings. They are used to coat laboratory equipment, furniture, and wire goods. They are not outdoor durable.

Polypropylene

As a surface coating, polypropylene offers many of the same useful properties it offers as a plastic material. Because of its inert nature, polypropylene shows little tendency to adhere to metal or other substrates. This makes it necessary to chemically modify natural polypropylene when it is used as a coating powder, so that adhesion of the coating to the substrate can be achieved. Water quenching after the heated flow-out cycle is common to prevent cracking.

Nylon

Nylon powders are typically based on type 11 nylon resin. They generally offer a tough coating with excellent abrasion and impact resistance, plus a low coefficient of friction when applied over a suitable primer. It is common to utilize a water quench when coating with nylon to improve physical properties and appearance. An interesting use of nylon as a coating powder is in the field of mechanical design. The unique combination of a low coefficient of friction and good lubricity makes nylon ideal for sliding and rotating bearing applications such as automotive spline shafts, relay plungers, shift forks, and other bearing surfaces on appliances, farm equipment, and textile machinery.

Polyvinyl Chloride

Polyvinyl chloride (PVC) coating powders have good exterior durability and provide coatings with a medium-soft feel and glossy surface. They bond well to most metal substrates when applied over a suitable primer. PVC coatings can offer good economics and withstand the stress of metal-fabrication operations such as bending, embossing, and drawing. Among uses for PVC coatings are furniture, shelving, tanks, and fencing.

Thermoplastic Polyester

Thermoplastic polyester powders have good adhesion to most metal substrates without requiring primers. They also exhibit good exterior durability. Thermoplastic polyester powders have been used as coatings for such items as outdoor-metal furniture and equipment.

Ethylene Acrylic Acid Copolymer

Coating powders with a base of ethylene acrylic acid (EAA) copolymer offer good adhesion and corrosion resistance, and result in a tough, damage-resistant film with excellent exterior durability. Their diverse end uses include wire, sporting goods, marine fittings, valves, and more.

Surlyn®

Coating powders based upon Surlyn® resins provide a high level of film toughness and resistance to chemicals and abrasion. An example of the toughness of this resin is its use for covering golf balls. Other common uses for Surlyn include shatter-resistant glass containers, outdoor furniture, and marine hardware.

THERMOSET COATING POWDERS

Thermosetting coating powders differ greatly from the thermoplastic variety. They are based initially upon lower-molecular-weight solid resins. When heated, thermoset-coating powders melt, flow, and cross-link chemically to form products that react to higher molecular weights. Cured coatings have different chemical structures than basic resins. Newly formed cured materials are heat stable and will not remelt to liquid after further exposure to heat. Powders based on more brittle resin systems can be ground into fine particles, in the range of 0.0004–0.0016 in. (10–40 μm) or less. Due to the rheology of these resin systems, they can produce thin paint-like coatings in the range of 0.001–0.003 in. (25–75 μm) with properties equivalent or superior to coatings produced from liquid-compliance technologies.

A technological expansion of thermoset-coating powders has continued over many years. Quite often, more than one generic type of coating powder can be custom formulated to meet specific end uses. The final choice of coating powder, of course, depends on economics and performance, and must be arrived at through cooperation between powder suppliers and users.

Epoxy-resin-based Systems

Epoxy powder is a prominent type of thermoset coating with a wide range of formulation latitude. It is appropriate for both thick-film functional end use and thin-film decorative use. Cross-linking systems are similar to those used in epoxy adhesives or two-part-epoxy paints; most are designed to be stable at room temperatures.

Functional Epoxies

The primary uses of thick-film functional epoxies are for electrical insulation and corrosion protection. In insulation use, epoxy powders form a tough layer that exactly follows the contours of an electrical component. It bonds to the part surface to become a permanent integral insulation that is free of voids and of low bulk. Typical applications include automobile alternators, electric motors, and switch gears.

For corrosion protection, epoxy powders are low cost and maintenance and offer long-lasting protection against most chemically aggressive environments. They provide a protective coating on underground gas and oil-field distribution piping. Epoxy powders, having resistance to high temperatures and pressures, are used as coatings for lining the inside of underground pipes for drilling oil. Epoxy-coated reinforcing steel bars (for highway and bridge decks) offer significant corrosion protection. They require high-speed application, a fast cure, and cool storage and shipment to prevent reaction advancement in the package.

Thin Film Coatings

Thin film coatings, generally less than 0.005 in. (127 μm) are formulated to produce highly attractive coatings of various gloss levels or surface textures, while retaining the inherent toughness, corrosion resistance, flexibility, and adhesion characteristics of the epoxy-resin family. Many advances in cross-linking chemistries of epoxies provide formulators with a wide range of film and appearance properties. The range of cure conditions, bake times, and temperatures, has especially been broadened. Epoxy powders that can be baked as low as 220° F (104° C) for a period of 10–30 minutes, or for a very short time at much higher temperatures in a conventional oven are available. A good example of this is the application of epoxy powder to screen wire, where a good combination of fast cure and thin film-forming ability is required.

Despite an excellent combination of mechanical, corrosion, or chemical-resistance properties, epoxy powder presents a weakness due to relatively poor exterior durability. Epoxy coatings, whether the original form is powder or liquid, will exhibit rapid gloss loss and chalking after only several months of exterior exposure. Although a weathered-epoxy coating may look unsightly, it may still maintain its mechanical, corrosion, and chemical-resistance properties well beyond the loss of appearance. Therefore, decorative epoxies are restricted to internal uses or areas of very little UV exposure, but this still leaves a large number of possible application areas for epoxy powders. Because of their combination of toughness, corrosion, and chemical-resistance properties, epoxy powders are used in the major-appliance industry. For example, in some applications white epoxy powder has replaced porcelain on refrigerator interiors and wire shelving, providing advantages and cost savings. One advantage is the elimination of cracking and chipping, such as that found with more brittle porcelain coatings that are handled roughly.

For refrigerator interiors, there is a cost savings in the type of substrate that can be used in the liner construction. Porcelain requires low-carbon steel, which must be thoroughly pickled through as many as 14 stages. Powder coating can use iron- or zinc-phosphated cold-rolled steel. Since porcelain must be fired at temperatures around 1,500° F (816° C) and thermoset epoxy powders normally bake at around 375° F (191° C), considerable energy savings are realized. Other areas of epoxy powder use in the appliance industry include the interior coating of dryer drums and microwave oven cavities. Similarly, the properties of epoxy coating powders make them very suitable for automotive parts such as oil filters, springs, and other components where sunlight exposure durability is not important.

Typical epoxy applications include fire extinguishers, shelving, toys, transformer cases, refrigerator liners, primers, dryer drums, bathroom fixtures, microwave ovens, refrigerator racks, mixers, and blenders. Others include sweepers, fertilizer spreaders, sewing machines, screening, power tools, oil filters, room air conditioners, automobile springs, office furniture, hospital equipment, instrument cases, bus seat frames, garden tools, business machines, bottles, and kitchen furniture.

Typical properties of epoxy powders are listed in Table 2-1.

Epoxy-polyester Hybrids

Epoxy resins will cross-link through a reaction with certain acid-functional polyester resins. In coatings based upon this system, the nature of the film and use of the finished article are different from that of straight epoxy powders. The term "hybrid" fits well to describe this combination of polymers.

Table 2-1. Typical properties of epoxy powder

Property	Range
Hardness (pencil)	HB–7H
Impact resistance, lbf/in. (N/m)	60–160 (10,508–28,020)
Gloss (60° meter)	3–100+
Color	All colors, clear and textures
Salt spray	1,000+ hours obtainable*
Condensing humidity	1,000+ hours obtainable*
Cure range (typical 0.002 in. [51 μm] film—time at metal temperature)	3 minutes at 450° F (232° C) 25 minutes at 250° F (121° C)

* Environmental resistance properties are a function of the total coating process, including substrate and pretreatment quality.

Epoxy-polyester hybrids (once considered simply an extension of the epoxy family) utilize a high percentage of polyester, most often more than half of the resin. The properties of hybrid coatings are more closely akin to epoxies than polyesters, with a few notable exceptions. They show similar flexibility in terms of impact and bend resistance, but produce softer films. Their corrosion resistance is comparable to epoxies in many cases, but their resistance to solvents and alkali is generally inferior to pure epoxies.

One advantage of hybrids over epoxies is a much greater resistance to overbake yellowing in the cure oven, which is due to the favorable influence of the polyester component. The polyester also introduces improved resistance to yellowing from UV-light exposure, though hybrids are still not suitable for long-term use outdoors. Outdoors, these coatings will lose gloss and begin to chalk nearly as fast as an epoxy powder.

Another advantage of epoxy-polyester coating powders is their good electrostatic-spray characteristics. They can be applied with excellent transfer efficiency and show good penetration into corners and recesses.

An epoxy-polyester hybrid should certainly be considered along with the epoxy family for thin film decorative use. Applications for epoxy-polyester hybrids include toolboxes, oil filters, air cleaners, farm equipment, air conditioner housings, fire extinguishers, transformer covers, electrical-control boxes, toys, screening wire, hot-water heaters, radiators, power tools, shelving, surface primers, office furniture, and grain storage bins.

Typical properties and ranges of epoxy-polyester hybrid powders are listed in Table 2-2.

Polyester

Polyester coating powders used commercially in the US are of two basic types with various curing mechanisms: hydroxyl-functional polyester (urethane) and carboxyl-functional polyester. Both systems offer wide ranges of properties and economics, including super-durable varieties that are capable of withstanding significantly extended times outdoors before surface deterioration begins.

Hydroxyl Polyester (Urethane)

Cured, hydroxyl-functional polyester powder (urethane) is chemically similar to exterior-use urethane paints used on aircraft, buses, trucks, and railroad cars. Powder coatings of this type combine an outstanding thin-film appearance and toughness with excellent weathering properties.

Table 2-2. Typical properties of an epoxy-polyester hybrid powder

Property	Range
Hardness (pencil)	HB–3H
Impact resistance, lbf/in. (N/m)	60–160 (10,508–28,020)
Gloss (60° meter)	10–100+
Color	All colors, clear and textures
Salt spray	1,000+ hours obtainable*
Condensing humidity	1,000+ hours obtainable*
Cure range (typical 0.002 in. [51 μm] film—time at metal temperature)	10 minutes at 400° F (204° C) 25 minutes at 300° F (149° C)

* Environmental resistance properties are a function of the total coating process, including substrate and pretreatment quality.

Typical curing for hydroxyl-polyester powder is 20 minutes at 375° F (191° C) or 10 minutes at 400° F (204° C). This is another area of thermoset coating chemistry that historically has expanded well within North America. Modern developments in cure chemistry have made it possible to obtain good film properties at lower temperatures, as low as 320° F (160° C) for 20 minutes. However, when lower-cure-temperature systems are considered, care should be taken to assure that properties such as hardness and exterior durability are maintained at levels adequate for the end use.

Hydroxyl-polyester chemistry lends itself to good performance with a thinner film-thickness range of 0.001–0.003 in. (25–76 μm). Thicker films tend to exhibit poorer mechanical properties such as impact resistance and flexibility. Hydroxyl polyesters are true competitors to high-quality liquid paints in respect to thin-film appearance.

Many hydroxyl polyester powders release an emission during cure, 1–5% by weight, or more. This is due to e-caprolactam or to other cure-reaction-blocking agents, which are present for long-term package stability. Emissions must be vented from a bake oven to prevent fouling or appearance contamination.

One major use of hydroxyl-polyester powders is in the coating of lighting fixtures, where excellent flow at a minimal film thickness leads to high reflectivity. Other areas of use include furniture, wheels, boat trailers, garden tractors, and other applications requiring exterior durability. In the appliance industry, hydroxyl-polyester powders are used as a porcelain replacement on range side panels. This material meets all of the requirements of the industry's exterior finishing specifications.

Applications for hydroxyl polyester powder include automotive trim parts, garden tractors, range side panels and broilers, fluorescent light fixtures, ornamental iron, steel and aluminum wheels, air-conditioner cabinets, restaurant furniture supports, patio furniture, playground equipment, fence fittings, transformer cases, and chrome wheels and trim.

Typical properties of hydroxyl-polyester powder are listed in Table 2-3.

Table 2-3. Typical properties of hydroxyl-polyester powder

Property	Range
Hardness (pencil)	HB–6H
Impact resistance, lbf/in. (N/m)	20–160 (3,503–28,020)
Gloss (60° meter)	5–95+
Colors	All colors, clear and textures
Salt spray	1,000+ hours obtainable*
Condensing humidity	1,000+ hours obtainable*
Cure range (typical 0.001–0.002 in. [25–51 μm] at metal temperature)	10 minutes at 400° F (204° C) 20 minutes at 320° F (160° C)

* Environmental resistance properties are a function of the total coating process, including substrate and pretreatment quality.

Carboxyl Polyester

Carboxyl polyester is another primary type of polyester powder. It has a base of functional-carboxyl polyester resins. Its use emerged from technology developed in Europe. It was introduced in North America to fulfill the need for more versatility in exterior-grade coatings. Carboxyl-polyester products can be described as exterior-durable cousins of epoxy-polyester hybrids. Instead of using conventional epoxy resins to co-react with the polyester, low-molecular-weight triglycidyl-isocyanurate (TGIC) or a b-hydroxy-alkylamide (HAA) curing agent is used. Polyester constitutes a very high percentage of the binder and provides weathering at least comparable to urethane polyesters.

Carboxyl polyester powders are typically baked for 3–15 minutes at 350–400° F (177–204° C), but more recent formulations give cures as low as 280° F (138° C) with extended times. This could pose an advantage over urethane-cure polyesters in certain applications. The primary attributes of this type of polyester are excellent mechanical properties at any film thickness and improved edge coverage. Films of 0.002–0.005 in. (51–127 μm) offer excellent flow, gloss, and toughness. The appearance of this coating at thicknesses below 2 mils (50 μm) may be less smooth than a similarly pigmented polyester urethane, but the difference is not necessarily great. Over-bake color stability is also excellent. For carboxyl polyesters, adhesion and corrosion-resistance properties are comparable to hydroxyl polyesters, but resistance to chemicals and solvents can be less.

One application for this type of polyester powder is coating outdoor transformer cabinets where a combination of edge coverage through high film build and good exterior durability is required. Typical applications of carboxyl-polyester powders are irrigation pipe and fixtures, fence poles and fittings, outdoor furniture, lawn and garden equipment, air-conditioning units, aluminum extrusions, steel and aluminum wheels, transformers, wire fencing; or any post-forming application requiring that an end product be able to withstand harsh weather conditions.

Typical properties and ranges of carboxyl-polyester powders are listed in Table 2-4.

Acrylics

Acrylics constitute another generic group of thermoset powders that exhibit exterior durability. In the early days of powder coating, imported acrylics established a good reputation for exte-

Table 2-4. Typical properties of carboxyl-polyester powders

Property	Range
Hardness (pencil)	HB–6H
Impact resistance, lbf/in. (N/m)	60–160 (10,508–28,020)
Gloss (60° meter)	5–95+
Colors	All colors, clear and textures
Salt spray	1,000+ hours obtainable*
Condensing humidity	1,000+ hours obtainable*
Cure range (typical 0.002–0.003 in. [51–76 μm] film—time at metal temperature)	3–10 minutes at 400° F (204° C) 30 minutes at 300° F (149° C)

* Environmental resistance properties are a function of the total coating process, including substrate and pretreatment quality.

rior durability combined with trouble-free application characteristics. Most acrylic coating powder sold in the US is hydroxyl-polyester- (urethane-) cured and glycidyl or epoxy-functional types.

Urethane acrylics require bake temperatures similar to hydroxyl-polyesters with minimum cure temperatures around 340° F (171° C). They are also characterized by an excellent thin film appearance and, unlike liquid acrylic paints, retain a level of flexibility for impact resistance with excellent hardness.

Acrylic powders have good alkali resistance, which is an important trait for use on appliances. On range sides, for example, they may come into contact with alkali oven-cleaning compounds, or on washing machines, hot detergent may contact them.

Acrylic powders demonstrate extremely good electrostatic spray properties, providing for very controllable thin film applications. As a class, acrylics are more sensitive to substrate quality than other thermoset-coating powders, and many are not compatible with other powder-coating chemistries.

Typical applications of acrylics include range-side panels, aluminum extrusions, refrigerator cabinets and doors, microwave ovens, garden tractors, dishwasher exteriors, washing-machine parts, and automotive trim.

Table 2-5 lists typical properties of acrylics.

Glycidyl methacrylateacrylic (GMA) requires a minimum cure temperature of around 300° F (149° C). These coatings have ex-

Table 2-5. Typical properties of acrylics

Property	Range
Hardness (pencil)	2–3H
Impact resistance, lbf/in. (N/m)	40–100 (7,005–17,513)
Gloss	10–90
Color	All colors, clear and textures
Salt spray	1,000+ hours*
Condensing humidity	1,000+ hours*
Cure range (typical 0.0015 in. [38 μm] film—time at metal temperature)	10 minutes at 400° F (204° C) 25 minutes at 350° F (177° C)

* Environmental resistance properties are a function of the total coating process including substrate and pretreatment quality.

cellent thin film appearance and flexibility in the form of impact resistance.

GMA acrylics make the most water-white-clear powder coatings and are used for various automotive and hardware applications that rely upon this high clarity.

Typical applications of GMA acrylics include automotive trim coatings, clear coating for aluminum wheels, motorcycles, and automotive prime surfaces.

Typical properties of GMA acrylics are listed in Table 2-6.

Silicone and Modified-silicone Coating Powders

Silicone and modified-silicone coatings can withstand operating temperatures from 400° F (204° C) to over 1,000° F (538° C). The material has found applications in areas from food-contact cookware to engine-exhaust systems. Typical properties and ranges of silicone powders are listed in Table 2-7.

Other Polyesters

Many polyester coating powders are based on cross-linking chemistries that provide additional versatility in terms of specialty, appearance, application, curing, film, physical, and/or economic properties. Some of the newer systems are proprietary or limited in availability and must be discussed directly by users and suppliers.

Table 2-6. Typical properties of GMA acrylics

Property	Range
Hardness	H–2H
Impact resistance, lbf/in. (N/m)	60–160 (10,508–28,020)
Gloss	10–95+
Colors	All colors, clear and textures
Salt spray	1,000+ hours
Condensing humidity	1,000+ hours
Cure range (time at metal temperature)	5 minutes at 400° F (204° C) 25 minutes at 300° F (149° C)

Table 2-7. Typical properties of silicone powders*

Property	Range
Hardness	H–5H
Direct impact, lbf/in. (N/m)	20 (3,503)
Gloss	10–85
Colors	Black and others, depending on system
Cure schedule	15 minutes at 440–500° F (227–260° C)
Operating temperatures	400 to over 1,000° F (204 to over 538° C) (type of substrate is critical)

* Can be formulated to comply with U.S. Food and Drug Administration (FDA) 175.300 requirements.

Typical applications of polyester powders include air-conditioning units, farm equipment, wire fencing, aluminum extrusions, transformers, and appliances (precoated metals).

Typical properties and ranges of polyester powders are listed in Table 2-8.

RADIATION-CURED POWDERS

Due to extremely short cure-cycle times for radiation-cured powder coatings, many items previously thought unsuitable for

Table 2-8. Typical properties of polyester powders

Property	Range
Hardness (pencil)	F–2H
Impact resistance, lbf/in. (N/m)	60–160 (10,508–28,020)
Gloss (60° meter)	20–90
Color	All colors, clear and textures
Salt spray	1,000+ hours
Condensing humidity	1,000+ hours
Cure range (time at metal temperature)	10 minutes at 400° F (204° C) 30 minutes at 375° F (191° C)

powder coating are now worth considering. The magnitude of the cure-time reduction allows the footprint of the coating line itself to be much smaller than early conventional designs that included large ovens. The nature of radiation curing, however, requires a clear line of sight from the emitter to the surface being cured. This requirement can limit the use of radiation curing to pieces that are simple with no shadow areas.

Polyester-coating powders based on cross-linking chemistries that react under high-intensity ultraviolet (UV) light (rather than high temperatures) are available. These UV-cured powders must still experience short thermal exposure for melt and flow, but their final cure is accomplished in a matter of seconds as the film is exposed to high-intensity UV. The low temperatures and short time periods required to melt and flow these coating powders makes them very suitable for use on substrates that are sensitive to too much heat, such as wood, plastic, or assemblies. As a result, UV-cured powders are utilized initially on these substrates for such end uses as furniture, fixtures, flooring, and assembled electric motors.

The use of near infrared (NIR®) energy as a sole source provides for an almost-instantaneous melt, flow, and cure process. The NIR® process works for many existing basic powder chemistries. The nature of this energy band allows for a very quick (for example, a few seconds) heating of the powder layer, without a significant heating of the substrate. An early application of NIR-cure technology involved assembled and gasketed gas springs.

COATING SELECTION

Industrial finishes are often custom formulated to individual end-user requirements. Successful application depends on close working relationships between users and suppliers. Selection should be strictly on the basis of demonstrated film performance. This is because film performance of a thermoset-coating powder is completely dependent on the "bake" it receives in a particular plant, and on a particular substrate, with a particular degree of cleanliness and type of metal pretreatment. Many products in the marketplace tend to cross over historical guidelines. In the powder coating industry, new areas of formulation expertise are always developing that can stretch the characteristics of a particular generic type, making it a more economically viable alternative under specific plant circumstances.

A summary of the key properties of each generic type of thermoset-coating powder is presented in Table 2-9.

In selecting a thermoset-powder type, key factors such as demonstrated film performance, application characteristics, and cost-performance balance should be kept in focus.

SAFETY

No matter which coating powder is selected for a particular application, health and safety aspects of the material to be used must be fully determined. This information should be requested from the supplier in the form of a Material Safety Data Sheet (MSDS). It can be of great significance during the final application.

Table 2-9. Key properties of thermoset powder coatings

Epoxy	Tough and flexible Excellent chemical and corrosion resistance and mechanical properties Poor exterior color/gloss retention
Epoxy-polyester hybrids	Decorative film performance Very good chemical and corrosion resistance and mechanical properties Fair exterior color/gloss retention
Hydroxyl polyester (urethane)	Thin-film-powder applications Good chemical and corrosion resistance and mechanical properties Very good exterior color/gloss retention
Carboxyl polyester	Thicker film powder applications Very good chemical and corrosion resistance Excellent mechanical properties Very good exterior color/gloss retention
Other polyesters	Very good chemical and corrosion resistance Excellent mechanical properties Very good exterior color/gloss retention
Acrylic urethane	Thin-film-powder coatings Good chemical and corrosion resistance Poor mechanical properties Excellent exterior color/gloss retention
Acrylic hybrids	Decorative film performance Very good chemical and corrosion resistance Good mechanical properties Fair to good exterior color/gloss retention
Glycidyl methacrylate acrylic	Thin-film-powder coatings Good chemical and corrosion resistance and mechanical properties Excellent exterior color/gloss retention
Silicone epoxy, silicone acrylic	Operating temperatures from 400 to over 1,000° F (204 to over 538° C) Can be formulated to fit FDA 175.300 applications

Economic Advantages

Energy and labor cost reductions, high operating efficiencies, and environmental safety factors are advantages of powder coating systems that attract more and more finishers. Great cost savings can be found in each of these areas.

When compared with liquid-coating systems, powder-coating systems have several obvious and significant economic advantages. There are also many advantages that may not appear significant by themselves but, when collectively considered, contribute substantially to cost savings. Although this chapter will try to cover all the cost advantages of powder coating, each individual application must be analyzed in light of its particular needs, and appropriate cost advantages must be adapted to the situation.

COST SAVINGS

The specific areas covered relative to the economic advantages of powder-coating systems are:

- energy savings,
- labor-cost savings,
- high operating efficiencies,
- capital costs,
- environmental factors, and
- plant safety.

Energy Savings

One of the most significant advantages of powder-coating systems is that they do not require special air makeup for the coating booth. Since powder contains no compounds that are volatile at room temperature, booth-containment air can be recirculated to the plant. This practice is quite advantageous to a plant where extreme weather conditions are prevalent (see Table 3-1). The cost of heating or cooling the booth-makeup air is sizeable in most coating operations, and considerable savings can result if this practice can be avoided (Table 3-2 and 3-3).

Another significant economic advantage of powder coating systems is the minimal amount of oven ventilation required, versus the higher amount of ventilation needed for liquid coatings such as waterborne, high solids, and electrocoating. The National Fire Protection Association (NFPA) 86-A requires that 10,000 standard cubic feet (SCF) (283.2 m^3) of air be exhausted from the oven for each gallon (3.785 L) of solvent load; the NFPA recommends that only 1,500 SCF (42.48 m^3) of air be exhausted for one pound (0.45 kg) of volatiles in sprayed powder (see Table 3-1). Generally, the amount of volatiles in powder is minimal. Since this amount will vary from powder to powder, a user should look critically at this factor in any potential use analysis.

Labor-cost Savings

Labor-cost savings with powder coating systems depend on individual finishers' requirements. When powder is delivered to a user's plant, it is ready to use (no need to mix any solvents or catalysts prior to application, as is necessary for many liquid coatings). Once an application process is operating, there are no critical operating parameters to maintain, such as viscosity and pH, as is the case for many liquid coatings. Nor are there percent solids monitoring, specific-resistance problems, binder-to-pigment ratios, or milliequivalent (MEQ) levels (necessary for electrocoating systems). The level of skill and training required of operators for powder-coating systems is less than that needed for liquid systems, and significantly less than for electrocoat systems.

There also may be labor savings with the use of powder due to the better overall coverage that can be obtained with automatic powder-coating equipment (less or no manual reinforcement is required). This savings depends largely on production requirements and part configurations, but it is a factor to be considered.

Table 3-1. Economic advantages of powder coating (example)

Line No.	Variable	Explanation	High-solids Liquid	Powder
		Applied Material Cost		
1	Paint cost, $/gal (reduced)	Liquid / Powder, $/lb	21.00	2.40
2	Volume solids, %	Reduced	54	98
3	Specific gravity	Powder only		1.6
4	Theoretical coverage, ft²/lb at 100%	Liquid – Line 2 × 1,604 / Powder – 192.4/Line 3	866	120
5	Material utilization, %	See Table 3-2	80	95
6	Film thickness, mils	Average	1.2	1.5
7	Actual coverage, ft²/lb or gal	Line 4/Line 6 × Line 5	577	76
8	Applied cost, $/ft²	Line 1/Line 7	0.0364	0.0316
		Exhaust-spray Booth		
9	Booth openings, ft²		208	60
10	Face velocity, ft/min	Minimum average is 100 ft/min, 125 ft/min recommended	125	133
11	Exhaust, ft³/min	Line 9 × Line 10	26,000	Returned to plant
12	Air temperature, °F	See Table 3-3 / yearly average	50° F	50° F

Table 3-1. (continued)

Line No.	Variable	Explanation	High-solids Liquid	Powder
		Exhaust-spray Booth		
13	Plant air temperature, °F	Average during winter months	70	70
14	Temperature difference, °F	Line 12 − Line 13	20	20
15	Btu/hr required	Line 11 × Line 14 × 1.1* at 100% efficiency	572,000	0
		Exhaust-bake Oven		
16	Production, ft²/hr	Number of parts per hr × part surface area	6,000	6,000
17	Coverage, ft²/lb or gal	Line 7	577	75
18	Applied coating, lb or gal	Line 16/Line 17	10.4	80
19	Solvent load, gal or lb/hr	(100% − Line 2) × Line 18	4.8	1.6
20	Exhaust required, ft³/min	Liquid − Line 19 × 167.0[a] Powder − Line 19 × 250.0[b] (minimum 600 ft³/min)	801.6	600

*The constant 1.1 is found by multiplying 0.018 (Btu required to raise 1 ft³ of air 1° F at 100% efficiency) by 60 (converting ft³/min to ft³/hr). 1.08 is rounded to 1.1.

[a] 167 = 10,000 SCF (NFPA recommended) × 1 hr /60 min liquid
[b] 250 = 1,500 SCF (NFPA recommended) × 1 hr /60 min powder

Table 3-1. (continued)

Line No.	Variable	Explanation	High-solids Liquid	Powder
		Exhaust-bake oven		
21	Bake temperature, °F	Recommended cure	325	375
22	Plant temperature, °F	Line 13	70	70
23	Temperature difference, °F	Line 21 − Line 22	255	305
24	Heat required, Btu	Line 20 × Line 23 × 1.1*	224,850	201,300
		Conveyor and Part Heat Loss		
25	Temperature difference, °F	Line 23	255	305
26	Conveyor and tooling load, lb/hr	(Conveyor weight/ft + hanger and hook weight/ft) × conveyor speed × 60	5,760	5,760
27	Ware load, lb/hr	Line 16 × ware lb/ft²	3,600	3,600
28	Total load, lb/hr	Line 26 + Line 27	9,360	9,360
29	Specific heat load, Btu	Use: steel 0.125, iron 0.13, aluminum 0.248	0.125	0.125
30	Total load loss, Btu/hr	Line 25 × Line 28 × Line 29	298,350	356,850
31	Radiation loss, Btu/hr	Total oven surface area (ft²) × 0.03* + Line 25 (If outside use Line 12)	1,517,760	1,815,360

* Btu loss per ft²/hour with 4 in. insulation

Table 3-1. (continued)

Line No.	Variable	Explanation	High-solids Liquid	Powder
		Conveyor and Part Heat Loss		
32	Total heat loss, Btu/hr	Line 30 + Line 31	1,816,110	2,172,210
		Total Energy Cost		
33	Exhaust-spray booth, Btu/hr	Line 15	572,000	0
34	Exhaust-bake oven, Btu/hr	Line 24	224,850	201,300
35	Conveyor and part heat loss, Btu/hr	Line 32	1,816,110	2,172,210
36	Oven make-up, Btu/hr	Line 20 × Line 14 × 1.1*	17,635	13,200
37	Total, Btu/hr	Line 33 + Line 34 + Line 35 + Line 36	2,630,595	2,386,710
38	Energy cost, gas $/hr	(Line 37/1,000,000)/ Table 3-2 × Cost/ 1,000,000 ft³	19.73	17.90
39	Energy cost, electric, $/hr	(Line 37/3,415)/Table 3-2 × Cost/KWh		

30

Table 3-1. (continued)

Line No.	Variable	Explanation	High-solids Liquid	Powder
		Labor and Maintenance Costs		
40	Labor costs with fringe, $/hr	A. Supervision	15.00	15.00
		B. Paint mix	12.00	
		C. Painters—liquid (2 operators)	27.00	
		D. Painters—powder (2 operators)		27.00
41	Total operator labor, $/hr	Total of line 40	54.00	42.00
42	Clean-up cost, $/hr	(Clean-up man-hours per shift × labor $/hr)/ operating hr/shift	1.72	0.60
43	Available sludge, gal or lb/hr	Line 18 × (100 − Line 5) × Line 2	1.12	3.92
44	Sludge cost, $/hr	Line 43 × disposal cost/gal or lb	4.23	Not applicable
45	Maintenance cost, $/hr	(Maintenance hr/yr × maintenance $/hr) + yearly replacement parts costs + operating hr/yr	5.92	2.53

Table 3-1. (continued)

Line No.	Variable	Explanation	High-solids Liquid	Powder
		Labor and Maintenance Costs		
46	Filter cost, $/hr	(Filter cost × lb of filters per year) + operating hr/yr	0.96	Not applicable
47	Labor and maintenance, $/hr	Line 41 + Line 42 + Line 44 + Line 45 + Line 46	67.95	49.05
		Cost Summary: Annualized Dollars		
	Material costs, $	Line 8 × Line 16 × operating hr/yr	425,880	374,400
	Energy costs, $	Line 38 × operating hr/yr	38,474	34,905
	Labor and maintenance costs, $	Line 47 × operating hr/yr	130,319	88,004
	Total operating costs, $		594,673	497,309
	Annualized cost/ft^2, $	Total operating costs/ (Line 16 × operating hr/yr)	0.0508	0.0425
		Other Costs to Consider		
	Depreciation			
	Tax/Energy credits			
	Reject/rework costs			
	Safety costs			
	Health consideration costs			

Table 3-2. Fuel efficiency

Fuel	Coal	Oil	Electricity	Gas Direct Fire	Gas Indirect Fire
	Heat Content, %	Heat Content, %	Heat Content, %	Heat Content, %	Heat Content, %
Efficiency	2,400,000 Btu/ Ton 50	142,000 Btu/ Ton 75	3,415 Btu/ KWh 75	100,000 Btu/ Therm 90	100,000 TRU/ Therm 80

High Operating Efficiencies

Economic advantages resulting from higher operating efficiencies are many and varied, depending on the particular operation. The most significant advantage is the material usage efficiency. Fluidized bed operations are inherently 100% efficient, although some loss may result from factors such as dragout and excessive film. Electrostatic-spray operations are usually considered to be 50–80% efficient at first use of the powder. That is, from 20–50% of powder is oversprayed and, if collected, it can be reused satisfactorily. Since oversprayed powder can be reclaimed during an application process and later reused, overall material utilization in the range of 95–98% can be achieved (see Table 3-4). By comparison, liquid spray-coating systems achieve material-usage efficiencies of only 20–90%. With electrocoating, 98–99% efficiency levels are possible.

Since powder greatly reduces drip, run, or sag, a significantly lower reject rate can be achieved. If badly sprayed parts are discovered prior to curing, they can simply be blown clean with an air gun, and then recoated. Since there is no flash-off time required when using powder coatings, a finisher can use the saved plant space more efficiently and economically. In addition, there is less chance of particulate and dust contamination, which normally would take place during the flash-off period. Less contamination results in fewer rejected powder-coated products.

Powder coating can achieve equal or superior film properties compared to liquid coating—in most cases with only one coat, thus eliminating the need to prime a part prior to applying the top

Table 3-3. Average temperature, °F (Canadian cities are in °C)

Location	Average*	Location	Average*
Albany, NY	48	Memphis, TN	62
Albuquerque, NM	55	Miami, FL	75
Atlanta, GA	62	Milwaukee, WI	48
Baltimore, MD	56	Minneapolis, MN	45
Bismarck, ND	41	Mobile, AL	68
Boston, MA	50	Montreal, Quebec	7
Buffalo, NY	47	Nashville, TN	60
Burlington, VT	45	New Orleans, LA	70
Calgary, Alberta	4	New York, NY	52
Cheyenne, WY	45	Oklahoma City, OK	60
Chicago, IL	50	Omaha, NE	51
Cleveland, OH	49	Philadelphia, PA	54
Columbia, SC	64	Phoenix, AZ	70
Concord, NH	44	Portland, ME	46
Dallas, TX	66	Providence, RI	50
Denver, CO	50	Quebec, Quebec	5
Des Moines, IA	50	Rapid City, SD	47
Detroit, MI	49	Reno, NV	50
Great Falls, MT	46	Richmond, VA	58
Hartford, CT	50	St. Louis, MO	50
Honolulu, HI	75	Salt Lake City, UT	51
Houston, TX	69	San Francisco, CA	56
Indianapolis, IN	53	Seattle, WA	52
Jacksonville, FL	69	Toronto, Ontario	8
Juneau, AK	42	Vancouver,	
Kansas City, MO	55	British Columbia	11
Little Rock, AR	62	Washington, DC	56
Los Angeles, CA	63	Wichita, KS	57
Louisville, KY	57	Winnipeg, Manitoba	3

*Source: Weather Bureau/Department of Commerce

Table 3-4. Material utilization

System	Conventional Liquid	Electrostatic Liquid	Disc or Bell Liquid	Electrostatic Powder
Utilization efficiency, %	40	50–70	80–90	95–98

coating. In addition, powder coating develops a full cure during the baking cycle, and it usually resists abuse upon leaving the oven better than liquid coatings. This results in less damage during handling, assembling, and packaging operations. It also decreases the need for touch-up. The reject rate is lower as well. Both contribute to savings.

Another positive aspect of using powder coating systems is that the amount of space required to store powder is considerably less, in most cases, than the space required for an equivalent liquid coating system. This allows for more productive and efficient use of available plant space.

Capital Costs

Capital costs associated with installing powder-coating systems are becoming more competitive with the costs of installing liquid-coating systems. Today they are well below those required for an electrocoating system. There is an additional cost for the laboratory equipment necessary for maintaining an electrocoat tank. In many cases, finishers are experiencing a one-year or less payback period after installing a powder-coating system.

Environmental Factors

In some cases, it may be more difficult to put a dollar figure on the economic advantages of powder coating when considering the environmental factors. However, there are significant factors that can be readily measured. Since there are effectively no solvents in powder coating, and as much as 70% of various solvents in a conventional coating, powder coating can achieve an environmentally "clean" finishing line.

As regulatory agencies further limit the amount of solvent emissions allowed, more finishers using liquid coatings systems must install costly afterburners to incinerate the emitted solvents. In almost every case, a solvent only adds to the cost and detracts from the properties of a cured coating. Another significant environmental factor is the increased difficulty and cost of disposing of the hazardous waste generated by a liquid coating application. In some cases, it is nearly impossible and is a responsibility that lingers for years.

Plant Safety

Consider the economic advantages of powder coatings in conjunction with plant safety. Since there are effectively no solvents in a powder coating, the significant reduction in fire risk could reduce a plant's insurance premiums considerably. In addition, any spillage of powder outside the coating booth can be safely and easily removed by an industrial vacuum cleaner fitted with an air-driven or dust-tight electric motor. There is also a reduced health hazard to the operator in a powder coating system, since there are no solvents to cause nose, mouth, throat, skin, or eye irritations.

There have been rare cases where a powder caused skin irritation. Powders can be abrasive by continued contact with contaminated clothing or gloves, and proper care should be taken. Problems can be avoided by washing with soap and water. The improved worker environment can result in lower employee absenteeism, which could be a significant economic advantage.

APPLICATION EVALUATION

Published material often gives cost justifications for powder, with comparisons to liquid. The most important figure in such evaluations is the net cost per square foot (m^2) or item to successfully coat the product with a suitable finish.

When considering costs, the entire finishing system, starting at the entrance area and including everything that creates cost for the manufacturer throughout the expected life of the product, must be considered. This should include items returned and product liability.

Some of the basic requirements to finish a part include:

- space and equipment for cleaning, pretreating, applying, and curing;
- manpower;
- coating material and supplies;
- energy washing, drying, spray-booth and oven-makeup air, and curing oven; and
- waste disposal.

There are many economic advantages of powder coating that should be considered. The individual requirements and needs for each powder coating application often can involve a different emphasis on each considered area, be it energy, labor, operating efficiency, environment, or safety.

four

Surface Preparation

The highest quality powder coating will provide excellent results only if pretreatment (cleaning, phosphatizing, and conversion coating) is done correctly and the overall pretreatment system is maintained up to its potential. In powder coating, the pretreatment basics of cleaning, rinsing, phosphatizing, and seal rinsing are slightly more critical than their importance in liquid-coating systems.

To maximize the benefit derived from powder, the pretreatment system must provide to the powder booth a clean conversion-coated product in a dry state. Dryness is one aspect that is more critical to powder than liquid coatings. Solvent- and water-based coatings can tolerate higher degrees of surface moisture than powder coatings. Powder coatings will cover wet areas, but will be displaced upon baking, leaving the bare substrate exposed. The same situation, or a worse one, holds true for surfaces contaminated with oils.

Surface preparation encompasses more than just conditioning or improving a substrate to accept the powder coating. Other conditions to be considered include:

- soils on the substrate;
- water quality for bath makeup and rinsing;
- consistent or varying substrates;
- metals mix (ferrous, nonferrous, yellow metals);
- metal type (cast, extruded plate, coil, sheet, or combinations);
- upstream processes such as machining, welding, cutting, etc.;
- size, weight, dimensions, and configurations of product;
- system control, maintenance, and record keeping; and
- type and amount of waste generated, along with disposal options.

39

Considering all of the key elements involved in producing high-quality, powder-coated products, cleaning is the single most important to maximizing powder-coating results. The degree of cleaning or surface modification is open to wide interpretations and results in many differing qualities. For some applications, abrasive cleaning alone is suitable, especially if the final product requires adhesion properties that have short-to-medium duration periods.

Leading powder-coating and pretreatment manufacturers tend to agree that a high-quality, five-stage spray system of cleaning, phosphatizing, and final seal rinsing is the most suitable and preferred method of pretreatment for the widest range of substrates and coating chemistries. It is important for manufacturers to work closely with their pretreatment and powder coating vendors.

MECHANICAL CLEANING METHODS

Mechanical methods of cleaning can be generally applied to all types of surfaces since they involve abrasion of surfaces by scrubbing, sanding, grinding, tumbling, or vibrating with abrasive media and wet (slurry) or dry abrasive blasting. Along with a cleansing action (removal of loose soils and tightly adhering contaminants such as mill scale on steel), processes may be selectively performed in a manner that produces an etched or toothed surface to improve adhesion of coating films to the substrate. Prominent among methods used to achieve both purposes simultaneously is abrasive blasting. Methods and systems of surface preparation by dry-blast cleaning include:

- open airblast with sand or various slag-type abrasives;
- manual airblast in environmentally controlled enclosures (airblast rooms) with or without material-conveyor systems;
- automated centrifugal-wheel blast; and
- centrifugal-wheel and airblast systems, in tandem or at separate locations in the path of product flow.

Airblast

The practice of blasting parts for cleaning or improving material surfaces goes back many years. It was called sandblasting because it was accomplished by introducing ordinary sand into a column of high-velocity air supplied by an air compressor, and manually directing the stream of sand at the surface to be treated. However, because a wide variety of abrasives are commonly used, the process is more appropriately called *airblasting* or *nozzle blasting*.

Portable nozzle blast systems have been developed in which an abrasive, after it has impinged the surface, is entrapped at the blast head, recovered by vacuum, and recirculated. The result is a virtually dust-free blasting operation in the field. These developments have extended many benefits in varying degree, according to the nature of the blasting operation. Operating costs have been reduced through reuse of abrasives, automated processing, and/or improved working conditions for blast operators. Improved environmental conditions and reduced air pollution have resulted from the use of portable, recoverable abrasive-blast systems and blast enclosures. The capacity for processing greater numbers and types of parts, including very large parts in a shop operation has been increased.

Blasting with nozzles is a practical production process used in several industry classifications. In many situations, it is the only means of achieving the preparation process. Modern airblast 26 enclosures, automated blast nozzle systems, and other innovations in the airblast systems have contributed in large measure to achieving environmentally acceptable airblast processes.

Airless (Centrifugal-wheel) Blast

Introduced in the 1930s was a device that hurled abrasive material by centrifugal force. Machine systems available for various applications differ only in the means by which the product is conveyed through the blast, the number and size of blast wheels required, and the type of blast media used. All centrifugal-blast systems, whether for shop installation or for portable use, have the same six basic components:

1. a blast enclosure to contain the abrasive as it is thrown from the wheel and to prevent generated dust from escaping to surrounding areas;

41

2. a means of presenting the workpiece to the blast;
3. the wheel or wheels, in whatever size and number required for a specific application;
4. a means of capturing and recirculating the abrasive;
5. an airwash separator, which removes dust and abrasive too small to be effective and returns the cleaned and usable abrasive to a storage hopper; and
6. a dust collector that separates dust from the abrasive, and ventilates and removes dust from the blast enclosure.

For applications in which the type and shape of parts and the process requirements may be accommodated by centrifugal blasting, the economy benefit has been proven many times over. Production rates are greatly increased, and production costs are significantly reduced. Airless-blast cleaning operations are far less labor intensive and far more energy-efficient than airblasting operations. Uniformity of quality in the finished product is enhanced in automatic and environmentally clean operations.

Method Selection

Either method of abrasive blasting may be incorporated readily into continuous, in-line-conveyorized production cleaning and coating operations. Generally, the airless method is more productive and economical than airblast. In airblast systems, accelerating the abrasive particles (particularly the higher-density ferrous abrasives) requires high volumes of clean, dry, compressed air, which in turn demands high-energy input. Centrifugal-blast systems require only about 10% of the energy needed by airblast systems to throw equal volumes of abrasives at the same velocities. However, the shape (or configuration) of the workpieces may dictate the selection of airblast systems because of the ability to position individual nozzles to direct the blasts into nooks and crannies that may be shadowed from the blast pattern of the centrifugal wheel. Often, the two methods may be used in tandem to achieve the optimum result.

Successful abrasive-blast cleaning and/or finishing operations require judicious selection of the combination of blast system and abrasive media to achieve the desired finish on the material and configuration of the part to be processed.

Applications

Abrasive blasting involves high-velocity propulsion and direction of abrasive particles against surfaces of parts or products, to remove contaminants and/or otherwise condition the surfaces for subsequent final finishing operations. Typical uses of abrasive blasting include:

- removing contaminated surface layers;
- removing oxides, corrosion products, and mill scale;
- removing dry soils, mold, sand, and paint;
- removing buffs, scratches, and surface irregularities;
- providing an anchor pattern for better adhesion of paints or other coatings;
- producing a hammered or matte surface finish; and
- etching and carving of decorative finishes.

The types of materials and parts that are abrasive blasted to prepare the surface for subsequent finishing operations and/or to produce the desired final surface finish include:

- ferrous and nonferrous castings and forgings;
- rolled and formed shapes, and weldments;
- thermoplastic and thermosetting plastic parts;
- molded rubber parts; and
- diverse materials, including glass, wood, and leather.

Abrasives

Numerous types of materials can be prepared by abrasive blasting. Selecting blast media depends on the type of material, the product to be processed, and the nature of the surface finish to be produced. A wide range of abrasives is available. Naturally occurring abrasives generally referred to as *sands*, include silica sands, as well as heavy mineral sands, with little or no free silica, such as magnetite, staurolite, and olivine rutile. Others used for specialty-type operations include garnet, zircon, and novaculite. Generally speaking, the use of these materials is limited to nozzle-airblast systems. Mineral slags derived from metal smelting and electric power-generating slags (bottom ash) are a rapidly growing source of abrasives for cleaning new, corroded, or painted-steel surfaces.

As with sand, the use of these highly aggressive products is generally limited to airblast systems.

By-product abrasives are mainly agricultural in character. By-products such as walnut and pecan shells and peach pits are excellent for use in both air- and airless-blast systems for removing paint, fine scale, and other surface contaminants, without altering the metal substrate. Corncob particles are effective for removing surface contaminants such as grease and dirt, without destroying or altering a painted or bare-metal surface. Media of these kinds are also frequently used in deflashing molded rubber and plastic parts.

Manufactured abrasives may be nonmetallic. Included in this category are glass beads for peening and cleaning small, delicate parts, and plastic media commonly used (like agricultural by-products) for deflashing molded rubber and plastic parts. Materials such as aluminum oxide and silicon carbide are frequently used for specialty etching or for cleaning metals such as stainless steel, aluminum, and copper. Aluminum oxide is frequently used (primarily in airblast systems) for cleaning and etching steel.

The most commonly used manufactured abrasives are cut stainless-steel wire and aluminum shot. These are used principally for surface preparation and shot peening of nonferrous alloy parts.

Some manufactured abrasives are ferrous metals. Three general types are available for surface preparation: chilled cast-iron shot and grit, malleable-iron shot and grit, and cast-steel shot and grit. Of these, cast-steel abrasives are, by far, the most frequently used. Since they are available in broad ranges of size and hardness, these abrasives have applications ranging from deflashing rubber parts with shot to etching hardened steels with hardened grit.

Precautions

Soils that adhere to a blasted surface or to abrasive particles may be the source of defects in a subsequently applied coating, such as paint or enamel. It is extremely important to note that parts on which oil or grease is present cannot be properly blast cleaned. These substances resist removal and, in recirculating abrasive systems, may contaminate the abrasive itself. It is, therefore, essential that oil and grease deposits be removed by solvent wiping or degreasing methods prior to blast cleaning. Alternatively, chemical-cleaning methods may be employed.

Surfaces to be blast cleaned should also be dry, although traces of moisture can be tolerated when heat generated by the blast is sufficient to vaporize moisture. Larger amounts of moisture cause the dust fines generated to adhere to the part surface. Failure to remove such dust may cause defects in a coating system. Excessive moisture also causes dust to adhere to abrasive particles and, in a recirculating abrasive system, moisture will inhibit thorough airwash cleaning of the abrasive, as well as the removal of dust fines from the system.

The blast profile should be consistent. Situations where media is allowed to degrade, or where control is lacking, will result in incomplete scale and corrosion removal. This produces a non-uniform substrate and a subsequent decrease in ultimate powder-coating durability. Where there is a combination of non-uniform profile and low-mil build of powder, reduced corrosion protection is common. This is often caused by the profile of peaks that extends through a powder coating.

Advantages

Abrasive blasting has numerous advantages, especially when combined with subsequent aqueous conversion coatings or phosphatizing. The prepared substrate is void of scale, corrosion, and soils; it is uniform, and offers mechanical adhesion properties similar to those of chemical conversion coatings.

Mechanical blasting offers advantages over chemical removal when cleaning hot-rolled-steel substrates. It is faster, safer for workers and, when controlled, provides a more uniform profile that is less likely to re-oxidize. Abrasive- or glass-bead mechanical conditioning of nonferrous castings of zinc and aluminum is, in many cases, the easiest way to prepare the surfaces for powder coating.

Limitations

Abrasive-blasting equipment has many high-wear components that must be maintained on a frequent basis. The blasting media must be replenished and the spent media removed to provide consistent cleaning results. Upsets in system performance are likely if parts contaminated with excessive water, oil, or grease are inadvertently processed.

CHEMICAL SURFACE PREPARATION

The chemical surface preparation used in any particular application is closely related to the nature of the surface being cleaned and the type of contamination. Most surfaces that are powder coated after cleaning are either galvanized steel, steel, or aluminum. Since not all chemical-type preparations are applicable to all these materials, the process selected depends on the substrate material. The various chemical cleaning methods will be discussed and substrate-specific issues will be presented as applicable.

Chemical cleaning products are available in a wide range of acid, neutral, and alkaline formulations. A variety of chemical agents are used and may be formulated specifically for a particular substrate or range of substrates. Just as in mechanical cleaning, the chemical program can be optimized for a particular part or substrate, or it can be designed as a multi-metal process, changing from steel to zinc to aluminum, with little or no modification. Chemical cleaning products can be applied by power spray, immersion, electrocleaning, or hand wipe processes.

Power-spray Cleaning

Using the power-spray method, parts to be cleaned are suspended in a tunnel while the cleaning solution is pumped from a holding tank and sprayed under pressure onto parts. The cleaning solution is then continuously recirculated. Spray-pressure ranges from 4–40 psi (28–276 kPa). Parts may be in a fixed position, or moving on a conveyor. Power washing combines the mechanical forces associated with the spraying action with the chemical aspects of the cleaning solution. Spray cleaning is often the fastest and most effective means of removing heavy or difficult soils, although it may not be practical for very small parts.

The spray-cleaning process usually incorporates two or more spray stages that include the cleaning stage and a water-rinse stage. Parts to be cleaned are usually conveyed from one stage to the other after suitable exposure. Additional stages of cleaning and rinsing may be used if required. The chemicals in the baths are usually maintained at a temperature of 80–200° F (27–93° C). Parts are exposed to these chemicals for between 30 seconds and five or more minutes. Typical times are 30 seconds to two minutes for cleaning, and 30 seconds to one minute for rinsing. When a power-spray washer is used, parts to be cleaned are suspended in a housing with appropriate pumps and piping. A heated solution is pressure-sprayed on the soiled surface of the parts, it runs off, and then is diverted into a holding tank, where it is continuously recirculated through a pump back onto the parts. Spray pressure must be sufficient to provide complete coverage with solution, but not excessive enough to cause hanging parts to become dislodged from the rack or conveyor. Typically, spray pressure is 15–30 psi (103–207 kPa). Spraying parts simultaneously with equal pressure from two sides generally balances the applied forces and prevents parts from being constantly dropped in the spray stage.

A cleaner stage, followed by a rinse stage, is used for most work processed today. When heavily soiled surfaces are encountered or a higher degree of cleanliness is required, additional stages are used. Depending on the demands of the operation, spray cleaning is done in a number of combinations of stages including:

- two stages—clean/rinse;
- three stages—clean/clean/rinse;
- four stages—clean/rinse/clean/rinse; or
- four stages—clean/clean/rinse/rinse.

Combinations of alkaline, neutral, and acid cleaners may be used to further address specific cleaning conditions and requirements. Alkaline and neutral cleaners have the benefit of being compatible with mild steel. This allows the washer system to be constructed of less-costly materials.

Typical hot-process spray cleaners operate in the 140–160° F (60–71° C) range. Low-temperature cleaners nominally operate in the 90–120° F (32–49° C) range. When parts are carried by a conveyor, cleaner stage times of 45–60 seconds, and rinse stage times of 30–45 seconds are typical.

Immersion Cleaning

In the immersion cleaning method, parts to be cleaned are simply immersed in a solution of cleaner in a plastic, mild-steel, or stainless-steel tank. Providing some mechanical agitation of the solution may increase effectiveness in an immersion application. This can be accomplished by adding a motor-driven mixer, a recirculation pump, ultrasonic-sound waves, or by moving the parts themselves. Cleaning chemicals designed for immersion cleaning processes are often more aggressive than spray formulations. Immersion cleaners must be capable of dissolving and dispersing soils without the aid of strong mechanical forces. Immersion cleaning relies on heat and chemistry to remove soils, rather than the mechanical action of impingement pressure. Due to the reduced complexity of an immersion system, equipment cost is typically less than that of a spray system.

In the immersion process, the surface to be cleaned is immersed or dipped into a cleaning solution contained in a tank. Heat, agitation (mechanically or by means of ultrasonic cavitation), or the application of electric current to permit electrocleaning may be incorporated in this process. The ware is immersed in the cleaning solution until acceptable cleaning is obtained. Simple immersion cleaning followed by ultrasonic cleaning or electrocleaning is only used where cleaning requirements are very severe. Solution temperatures are usually 140–212° F (60–100° C). Typical immersion times are two to five minutes. Extended times of up to one hour may be used when heavy or difficult-to-remove soils are encountered. Concentrations of cleaning chemicals can vary widely. Highly concentrated, powdered formulations and liquid products are available. Powders should be dissolved prior to adding them to the process tank. The failure to first dissolve a powdered cleaner can result in concentrated deposits on workpieces, or a buildup of undissolved materials at the bottom of the immersion tank. Liquid formulations are generally easier to feed and control and may be pumped directly to a process automatically or manually.

Electrocleaning

Electrocleaning is a specialized version of immersion cleaning where a direct or slowly alternating current is passed through the solution. Parts to be cleaned are hung in the solution and are the anode, while other electrodes placed in the solution tank act as the cathode. Electrocleaning is more effective than plain immersion due to the scrubbing action of the gas bubbles produced at the surface of the part.

Generally speaking, precleaning of parts prior to electrocleaning is recommended. Precleaning is used to remove gross soils while electrocleaning acts as a fine-cleaning step to remove finely divided and difficult-to-remove soils such as metal fines and carbon deposits. This type of cleaning is only employed where soils and the degree of cleanliness warrant. It is most commonly used on cold-rolled-steel substrates to remove rolled-in metal fines and carbon.

Electrocleaning is often the last step (except for rinsing) prior to a plating operation, but it can be used in support of a powder coating process. It is not commonly used prior to phosphating of parts and cannot be performed in a spray system.

Hand Wiping

The hand-wiping method of cleaning combines the physical act of removing the soil from the surface by means of a cloth or sponge with the cleaning solution that helps to solubilize the soils. Hand wiping is only practical for a low to moderate number of workpieces, but may commonly be combined with mechanical cleaning or chemical cleaning to address part-specific problem areas. For some workpieces and soils, hand wiping can be the best stand-alone approach to cleaning.

Strong acid and alkaline, cleaning chemicals should be avoided for hand-wiping operations due to worker exposure and safety concerns. Gloves, coveralls, and faceshield may be used to safely apply strong chemicals by hand where necessary.

Liquid, moderately alkaline, cleaner solutions may be applied to the surface to be cleaned using a hand-held rag, brush, mop, etc. The "wetted" soil is allowed to soak for a period of time and is then spray rinsed with water and/or dried by rag wiping or blowing the surface dry with compressed air. The cleaner solution can be applied and reapplied until a sufficiently clean surface is obtained, which is then rinsed. Applied with a hand-held rag or brush, the solution is normally unheated or warmed only slightly by preparing the solution in hot water. Application should be made only to an area that can be handled by one person, to avoid streaking, drying, etc. Although a cleaning solution may be readily rinsed from the surface, if it is allowed to dry on the part, rinsing becomes much more difficult.

Spray-wand Cleaning

Spray-wand cleaning is a manual operation commonly employed for parts that are too large or heavy for processing in a conveyorized fashion. Cleaning solutions can be applied to a soiled surface by mixing the aqueous solution with hot water and spraying the mixture on the soiled surface through hand-held guns. Often these systems introduce the chemical into the water stream by a siphon device connected to the pump. This mixture is then heated using a heat source (natural gas, LP, oil, etc.) and heat exchanger coil. When sprayed, the cleaner solution is continuously applied to the soiled surface for a sufficient time to permit acceptable cleaning. The temperature of the cleaner solution is nominally controlled by a thermostat. When an elevated temperature is not required, diluted aqueous solutions can be sprayed on the soiled surface without turning on the heat source. Rinsing is usually accomplished by shutting off the chemical siphon valve and using just the hot water to remove any residual cleaning chemicals and soils from the part. The surface is either blown dry with compressed air, allowed to air dry, or dried in an oven. Application using a hand-held gun by one person should be made only to an area where adequate cleaning and rinsing can be obtained without streaking and drying.

Spray-wand cleaning is best performed in an enclosed area using adequate ventilation. Containment can be as simple as a plastic curtain or as durable as galvanized-steel or stainless-steel walls. In all cases, adequate ventilation must be used to ensure operator safety and to exhaust the vapors associated with this process from the plant airspace.

Normally, when a spray-wand cleaning process is employed, the chemicals are not recycled, but rather are discharged to a drain. Often these systems have pH balance and adjustment systems that automatically neutralize the discharge as it goes to drain. Local wastewater regulations must be adhered to when using a spray-wand system, as discharge must be compliant before going to drain.

Cleaning Chemistries

There are many variations in the equipment available for spray and immersion cleaning. To a certain extent, the features of the cleaning system determine some of the characteristics of the chemical cleaning formulation. The following discussion covers some of the different types of cleaning products commonly used.

Alkaline Cleaners

Cleaners are formulated across the entire pH range. Alkaline cleaners are at the high end of the pH scale. As a general definition, alkaline cleaners have a pH between 9 and 14. A pH between 9 and 11 will generally be considered a mild-alkaline cleaner. A pH above 11 is considered a strong-alkaline cleaner. Electrocleaners, one of the highest alkaline-cleaning products, have a pH of nearly 14 due to the large quantities of sodium and potassium hydroxide used to increase the electrical conductivity of the electrocleaning bath.

Alkaline cleaners are formulated differently depending upon the substrate. Those formulated for aluminum usually have a blend of mild-alkaline salts to avoid excessive attack of the aluminum surface. Aluminum will actually dissolve rapidly in highly alkaline solutions. Aluminum parts that fall off a conveyor into a strong-alkaline cleaner bath can completely dissolve in a matter of hours. This reaction may be used to chemically etch an aluminum surface, improve mechanical adhesion, or remove a difficult soil, but care must be taken to prevent excessive etching. A smutty residue forms on the aluminum surface during heavy etching as magnesium, silicon, and other alloying elements precipitate from the cleaning solution. For the same reason, highly alkaline cleaner formulations are not commonly used on zinc or galvanized substrates. The zinc surface is also etched by strong alkali but the surface will typically "burn" rather than completely dissolve. A burned zinc surface is generally characterized by a discoloration of the metal and often exhibits reduced receptiveness to conversion coating and painting. It is possible to avoid the undesirable effects of strong alkaline formulations on aluminum and zinc surfaces by limiting the concentration of the cleaner chemical, temperature of the bath, and contact time. Chemical inhibitors may be formulated into the cleaner to avoid excessive etch. This is extremely useful when a variety of substrates are processed. The dissolving action of the strong alkali prevents damage to the surface of the work. Time, temperature, and concentration are key process parameters for cleaning as well as all aspects of the surface preparation process.

Because steel surfaces are highly resistant to attack by aqueous alkaline solution, an extremely wide variety of strong-alkaline cleaners can be formulated. Strong-alkaline formulations can be used to strip difficult soils without damage to the base metal.

In general, combinations of phosphates, silicates, and carbonates, with varying amounts of caustic agents, may be formulated as cleaners. In addition, sequestering agents or chelating agents, dispersants, and one or more surfactants, nonionic or anionic, are used. Solvents are sometimes used in place of surfactants to remove oils but must be counted in the volatile organic compound (VOC) content of the product and hazardous materials content.

Neutral Cleaners

A neutral cleaner may be composed of only surfactants, neutral salts plus surfactants, or surfactants with other organic additives. A neutral cleaner may be defined as any cleaner which, in solution, would register 6–8 on the pH scale.

Just like alkaline cleaners, neutral cleaners are usually applied by using a minimum of two stages: the cleaning stage and a water rinse. Additional stages may be used if required. These solutions are used at a bath temperature range of 80–200° F (27–93° C). Typical bath temperatures are 120–160° F (49–71° C) for spray and 150–180° F (66–82° C) for immersion. The parts are exposed for 30 seconds to five or more minutes. Typical process times are one to two minutes for spray and two to five minutes for immersion.

Neutral cleaners are often not sufficiently effective to be the primary cleaner. They are more likely to be used as a precleaner to remove excess oil and grease or other heavy contamination. A neutral cleaner may be specified as the primary cleaner if the parts to be processed are minimally soiled, may be damaged by acid or alkaline cleaners, or if other specific plant conditions warrant.

Acid Cleaners

Acid cleaners are generally used for aluminum and steel substrates. Zinc is rapidly attacked by acid in much the same way aluminum is attacked by strong alkali, resulting in very high etch rates. Where heavy etching is a requirement, acid cleaning of zinc may be desirable, but it is not normally recommended. Mildly acidic cleaners may be used on zinc surfaces.

Acid cleaners are formulated from a much greater number of acidic compounds compared to alkaline cleaners. Potential acids include citric, acetic, phosphoric, sulfuric, nitric, oxalic, hydrochloric, hydrofluoric, and more. Mineral acids (for example, sulfuric or hydrochloric acid) are commonly used to remove rust, heat scale, and corrosion from steel. Organic acids and phosphoric acid, together with solvents, coupling solvent, and surfactants are used to clean (remove soils) and remove red rust and other corrosion. Among these organic acids, phosphoric is the most common. Other common components include mildly acidic salts and surfactants.

Properly formulated and applied, acid cleaners can remove surface oxides from aluminum and steel, improving the surface for subsequent pretreatment. Because most pretreatments are acidic in their chemistry, acid cleaners have the additional benefit of greater compatibility with subsequent processes. Acid cleaners excel in metal oxide removal but often fall short of alkaline cleaner performance when it comes to heavy oil and grease-type soils.

Acid cleaners are usually applied using a minimum of two stages, the cleaning stage and a water rinse. Additional stages may be used if required. Acid solutions are held at a temperature of 80–200° F (27–93° C). Typically 100–140° F (38–60° C) is the bath temperature for spray applications and 140–180° F (60–82° C) is used for immersion. Parts are exposed for 30 seconds to five or more minutes. Typically, exposure of one to two minutes is used for spray applications and two to five minutes for immersion.

CONVERSION COATING

Galvanized Steel

Iron phosphates or clean and phosphate (cleaner-coater) products can produce undetectable conversion coatings on zinc surfaces. Many multi-metal finishing lines use modified iron phosphates, which offer cleaning and leave a micro-chemical etch on zinc substrates to improve adhesion properties. Although very little phosphate is deposited, these products are suitable for providing cleaning and a degree of improvement in paint adhesion.

Many municipalities and states now have limits on zinc in plant wastewater effluent, forcing metal finishers to provide treatment of any solutions in which zinc substrates are processed.

The zinc-phosphate conversion coating is, perhaps, the highest quality coating that can be produced on a galvanized surface. To produce a zinc-phosphate coating on galvanized steel, special accelerating agents are required to activate the surface to receive the coating. These accelerators, also known as activators, deposit on the zinc surface creating "seeds" for crystallization. Once properly activated, the work is processed in the zinc-phosphating solution where the action of acidic phosphate compounds on the zinc surface generate the conversion coating—a crystalline zinc phosphate is "grown" on the clean substrate surface. In a typical seven-stage zinc-phosphating unit, the various stages are:

1. alkaline cleaner,
2. hot-water rinse,
3. activator,
4. zinc phosphate,
5. cold-water rinse,
6. post-treatment (either chromium or non-chromium type), and
7. deionized water rinse.

In the power-spray method of application, the parts to be coated are suspended in a tunnel while the solution is pumped from a holding tank and sprayed under pressure onto the parts. The coating solution is continuously recirculated with additional chemicals added to the bath as required.

In the immersion method of application, clean parts are simply immersed in a solution of the phosphating chemicals contained in a heated stainless-steel tank.

Phosphate coatings are usually applied by using five, six, or seven stages. The phosphate solution is held within a temperature range of 100–160° F (38–71° C) for immersion. The applied zinc-phosphate coating weight is typically in the range of 150–300 mg/ft^2.

A processing time of 30–60 seconds by spray and one to five minutes by immersion is usual. Phosphating solutions have a concentration of 4–6% by volume and are applied at spray pressures of 5–10 psi (34.5–68.9 kPa).

Zinc phosphate is often the best paint-base coating for galvanized steel and other cast zinc surfaces. In addition to iron and zinc phosphates for zinc surfaces, alternative conversion coatings include chrome chromate, complex oxide, and a variety of polymer and fluoacid-based chemistries. These products should be considered on an application-by-application basis. Consult with a pretreatment chemical supplier for more information on the latest developments in this area.

Aluminum

A standard iron-phosphate processing solution can only produce a coating on aluminum if certain accelerators are used, namely acidic fluorides. The coating produced, however, is not iron phosphate, but aluminum phosphate. In phosphating an aluminum surface, acidic chemical attack of the metal surface results in the dissolution of aluminum and the subsequent precipitation of aluminum phosphate. Iron phosphating of aluminum is most often practiced where aluminum is a minor component in a mixed-metal process.

In the power-spray method of application, parts to be coated are suspended in a tunnel while the coating solution is pumped from a holding tank and sprayed, under pressure, onto the parts. The coating solution is continuously recirculated and additional phosphating chemicals are added as required. In the immersion method of application, the parts are simply immersed in iron-phosphate coating solution contained in a mild steel or, preferably, stainless-steel tank.

A minimum of three application stages should be used for adequate quality; five for best quality. The solutions normally are held at a temperature of 98–120° F (37–49° C) for spray and 130–160° F (54–71° C) for immersion. Coating weights of 5–40 mg/ft^2 are normal. Parts are exposed to the chemicals for one to two minutes by spray and three to five minutes by immersion.

The aluminum-phosphate coating produced from an iron-phosphating solution is a relatively good paint base providing adhesion significantly better than material that has only been cleaned. The process is easy to operate and maintain, and can be applied in as few as three stages. However, the process cannot be used exclusively for aluminum without significantly decreasing the effective life of the bath. To maintain the proper balance of chemicals in the bath, some steel also must be processed. The balance of chemicals in the bath also can be maintained through the use of special proprietary additives.

A zinc-phosphate processing solution will produce a very good quality coating on aluminum. It is one of the best paint bases produced on an aluminum substrate. To adequately create zinc-phosphate coating on aluminum, a minimum of five operation stages are usually required. The temperature of the solution is between 108–160° F (42–71° C) for spray and 120–200° F (49–93° C) for immersion. Coating weights of 50–200 mg/ft^2 are typical. Times of one to three minutes by spray and two to five minutes by immersion are generally required.

A zinc-phosphate processing solution can be used exclusively for producing a conversion coating on aluminum. It is a very good paint base, but produces a substantial quantity of insoluble sludge. This sludge can deposit on heat-exchanger plate coils, causing a decrease in heat-transfer efficiency. It can also plug up the nozzles and piping in a spray application. It is necessary to clean out the zinc-phosphate-coating stage periodically. Sludge may be decanted in an off-line holding tank daily or weekly, depending upon production rates. Biannual or annual chemical clean-out of the processing stage is highly recommended.

Chromium-phosphate conversion coating is the most used paint base applied to an aluminum surface. Its adhesion and corrosion resistance properties are excellent and well documented (up to 5,000 hours salt-spray resistance is not uncommon). Chrome phosphate is widely used in the painting of aluminum extrusions. This treatment process is limited to treating only aluminum.

When aluminum parts are chromium-phosphate coated, usually five stages are used in the process. The solutions are held at a suitable temperature of 70–130° F (21–54° C). A coating weight of 20–100 mg/ft^2 is normal.

Chromium-phosphate conversion coating is superior to zinc phosphate as a paint base on aluminum. It exhibits better salt-spray resistance and offers improved adhesion and flexibility. Although the sludge produced by a chrome-phosphate process is substantially less compared to zinc phosphate, it is very tenacious, making clean-up difficult. Also, the chrome-phosphate process involves toxic heavy metal and hydrofluoric acid, which require care in handling to avoid exposure and must be disposed of properly. This corrosive process requires a stainless steel or suitable plastic tank and associated equipment.

Steel

Iron phosphate accounts for the majority of the steel conversion coating. A number of different proprietary compositions can be used to produce an iron-phosphate conversion coating on steel surfaces. These compositions are all mildly acidic. They are principally partly neutralized phosphoric-acid solutions with various accelerating agents, stabilizers, surfactants, and other ingredients added to them. Some formulations are available in a powdered form. When the functions of both cleaning and coating are desired in one stage, a detergent surfactant can be incorporated with the iron-phosphate composition in one package, or can be added separately at tankside, when required. Cleaner and iron-phosphate products, or cleaner-coaters, offer some compromise in the cleaning and conversion-coating capability of the process. Under many circumstances, these processes may produce excellent quality results with reduced capital investment compared to separate cleaning and phosphating operations.

Moderate or strong-acid proprietary compositions, capable of removing rust and containing surfactants and solvent to remove oils and soils, can be wiped or brushed on steel to produce a light-iron-phosphate coating. Aqueous solutions are applied using a rag or mop. The solution can be reapplied where and when necessary, until the surface is clean and free of rust, and the light-iron phosphate has developed. The time required is determined by what is needed for the manual application of the solution to a suitable area, to remove the soils, and produce the coating. The solution, applied by hand-held rag or brush, is normally unheated.

Spray-wand phosphating is best suited for extremely soiled substrates where the water and chemical displace tenacious oil, grease, and waxy soils as well as particulate matter. Although spray-wand cleaning and phosphating works well, the process is typically manual and the effective cleaning area is only as wide as each pass of the width of the spray-wand gun. This method of cleaning and iron phosphating is most commonly used where a small number of large objects are processed. Hot-water, high-pressure cleaning and phosphating handheld systems are gaining popularity with custom coaters and manufacturers of large substrates or products. This application equipment generally operates at a minimum of 800–1,600 psi (5,516–11,032 kPa), and at from 3–5 gallons per minute (GPM) (11–19 L/min) of solution. Temperature ranges from 140–200° F (60–93° C) at the nozzle tip, with chemical concentrations of from 1–3% by volume. Iron-phosphate coating weights can reach 35–45 mg/ft^2 meeting TT-C-490C Type II specification requirements. When considering the use of high-pressure, hot-water, handheld systems (spray-wand systems), it is important to have stainless-steel components as the phosphating solutions are acidic. Advances in this area also incorporate wet sandblasting attachments, which are effective in thoroughly cleaning weldments.

Iron-phosphate conversion coatings can be applied by immersion application methods. Where light soils are encountered, the cleaning and coating can be accomplished in one stage, preferably with the assistance of some form of agitation. In general, immersion iron-phosphate coatings will tend to look streaky and be of a light-gray-blue color. The phosphating process must be immediately followed by water rinsing to prevent flash rusting of the steel surface. Moderate to heavily soiled parts require cleaning and coating in separate stages, each followed by a water rinse. Parts can be cleaned and coated in two-to-five-minute time cycles if some form of agitation is used. Cleaner-coater processes can be operated at temperatures of 90–170° F (32–77° C). Low-temperature processes are generally not suitable for heavily soiled work. The operating temperature is normally controlled to meet the cleaning requirements of the soils encountered, and is influenced by the amount and type of agitation available.

Power-spray washers are the most widely used method of applying iron-phosphate coatings. Depending upon the soil conditions of the ware and the quality-level requirements, spray systems may consist of as few as two stages (cleaner-coater in one, water rinse in two), and as many as nine. Typical variations include:

- two stages—clean/coat, rinse;
- three stages—clean/coat, rinse, post-rinse;
- four stages—clean/coat, rinse, post-rinse, deionized water flush;
- five stages—clean, rinse, treat, rinse, post-rinse;
- six stages—clean, rinse, treat, rinse, post-rinse, deionized water flush;
- seven stages—clean, clean, rinse, treat, rinse, post-rinse, deionized water flush;
- eight stages—clean, rinse, clean, rinse, treat, rinse, post-rinse, deionized water flush; or
- nine stages—clean, rinse, clean, rinse, treat, rinse, post-rinse, deionized water rinse, deionized water flush.

Deionized water is commonly utilized in situations where available water quality is poor or maximum quality requirements dictate the need. The number of stages required is normally determined by the cleaning difficulty and the desired corrosion performance.

When a typical conveyor system is used, the cleaner stages will require 30–60 seconds; treatments require 45–90 seconds; and rinse/post-rinse/deionized water rinse requires 15–30 seconds.

Iron-phosphate treatments can be accelerated to produce good quality coatings at various temperature ranges. Low temperatures are 90–120° F (32–49° C) and hot processes 140–160° F (60–71° C). As the line is placed in operation, there is some thermal carryover, and rinse temperatures can approach to within 20–40° F (11–22° C) of the temperature of the preceding stages.

Where iron phosphate cannot meet quality requirements, zinc phosphate is the next step up in performance. A great number of different proprietary compositions can be used to produce a zinc-phosphate conversion coating on steel surfaces. These products are: acid solutions containing zinc; various acidic-phosphate compounds in aqueous solution; one or more accelerating agents, including chlorate and nitrate, with or without separate tankside additions of nitrite; or one or more modifying agents, grain-refining agents, coating-weight-control agents, etc. Many zinc phosphates are formulated with additional heavy metals such as nickel or cobalt to improve quality characteristics. However, these complicate the handling and disposal of the wastewater effluent.

With the more complex composition of the zinc-phosphate chemicals goes a more complex feed and control program. As mentioned previously, the zinc-phosphate program will produce significantly more sludge as compared to an iron-phosphate program. Although this further complicates the process, being prepared with a de-sludging program is the majority of the battle.

Proprietary zinc-phosphate-coating compositions are available for spray and immersion applications. The conversion coating deposited for paint-base quality is in the range of 150–300 mg/ft^2. Typical spray and immersion systems are composed of six stages: clean, rinse, activate, zinc phosphate, rinse, and post-rinse. Immersion zinc-phosphate coatings can be developed in two to five minutes, spray coatings in 45 seconds to two minutes. Temperature requirements of 90–160° F (32–71° C) are needed, depending upon the particular process. Higher temperatures will generally produce target coating weights in shorter times, but proper accelerators must be used.

As with iron-phosphate processes, power-spray-washer application accounts for the largest proportion of paint-base, zinc-phosphate-treatment processing. Depending upon a great many factors, including the nature and amount of soil, the rinsing and draining geometry of the ware, and the quality levels required, as few as five stages and as many as nine stages may be needed.

Proprietary zinc-phosphate-coating compositions have been formulated that can be brushed on clean steel surfaces. The surface must be cleaned prior to the application of the conversion coating solution by any of the usual methods. The brush-on treatment is applied, the coating is allowed to develop, and the ware is then rinsed with fresh tap water and dried. The brush-on treatment will produce an acceptable coating in two to five minutes. Compositions are typically applied unheated to a surface at room temperature. These treatments are particularly useful for making repairs on previously phosphated surfaces.

It is technically possible to produce a zinc-phosphate coating on steel by applying the coating product through a spray-wand system. However, due to the poor overall quality produced and the short life of the operating equipment, as well as sludging and scaling, this method of application is not used.

Powder Coating Application Methods

There are many methods available for applying powder-coating materials, with selection based on such factors as:

- product characteristics, including size of the part being coated, type of coating to be applied, desired or specified coating film thickness, reason for applying the coating, etc.;
- production quantities;
- number of colors used;
- means of conveying the part through the coating process, line speed, and racking configuration;
- means of applying the powder—automatically, manually, or in combination;
- available plant space, and
- capabilities of available powder-coating equipment to meet immediate and future needs.

Available methods range from simple fluidized beds to more sophisticated electrostatic spray processes. Each has particular advantages for specific coating applications. Generally, the most widely used and accepted powder application methods fall into the following categories:

1. fluidized powder-bed processes;
2. electrostatic fluidized-bed processes;
3. electrostatic powder spraying; and
4. other electrostatic-application methods, including discs and bells.

FLUIDIZED POWDER-BED PROCESSES

The fluidized powder-bed process was introduced in the United States in the late 1950s, and was the first powder-coating process used in a production mode. In this process, a preheated part is immersed into a fluidized-powder bed. The actions of heat, and the powder coming into contact with the part, result in the powder being melted and adhering to the heated part. The material-coating thickness on the part is determined by the part's temperature and length of time a part is in the fluidized-powder bed. Attaining the proper cure of the deposited powder may require post-heating the part if the residual heat is not sufficient to cure and flow the powder that adhered during the immersion process (Figure 5-1).

Construction

The fluidized bed is constructed as a two-compartment container, or tank, with the top open so that parts can be dipped into the powder fluidized within the bed. The upper compartment is used for storage and fluidization of powder. The lower compartment serves as an air plenum where compressed air is regulated and dispersed through a porous membrane separating the two compartments, as illustrated in Figure 5-2.

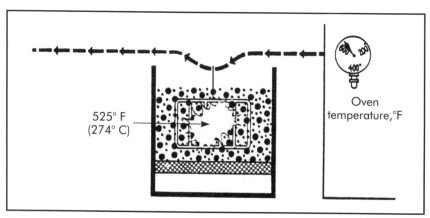

Figure 5-1. The part temperature is the only thing that is important. The temperature in the oven serves only to heat the part.

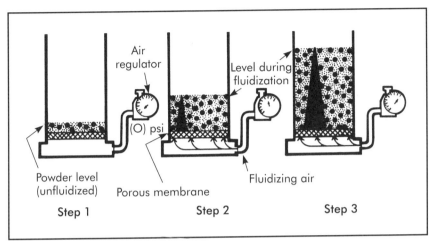

Figure 5-2. Fluidized bed.

The size of the fluidized bed depends on the size of the part to be coated. In the fluidized bed, the size of the tank and the volume of material must allow the part to be immersed below the upper level of the fluidized powder. Proper fluidization is governed by even distribution of air through the porous membrane or plate to create a lifting effect by agitating the powder material. Mechanical vibration of the container is sometimes used to enhance fluidization and reduce the possibility of air channeling and powder clumps. An important aspect of proper fluidization involves the quality of the compressed or turbine-blown air introduced to the fluidized bed. Clean, dry air is an absolute must. Oil, water, or pipe scale contaminants within the air supply would result in blocking, and possibly rupturing, the porous membrane, as illustrated in Figure 5-3. This results in uneven fluidizing distribution, which will ultimately affect the finish of parts being coated. Contamination of the powder material is also a distinct possibility in cases where clean, dry air is not used.

The fluidized bed should be constructed with smooth walls that are virtually free of seams, flanges, or other protrusions that could come into contact with the powder material. The porous membrane, or plate, can be constructed of any available porous material, although porous polyethylene works best. The size and thickness of the membrane should be sufficient to support the

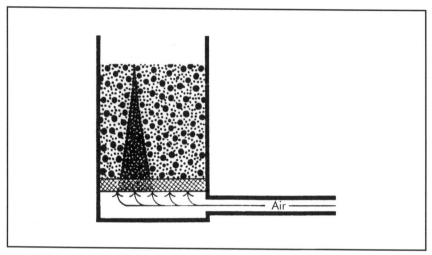

Figure 5-3. Blocked diffusion.

volume of powder material and provide complete fluidization to the interior of the porous bed. The electrical conductivity of the material used in bed fabrication is also important to help eliminate static charge. The container should be adequately grounded, to "bleed" off any static charge created by the frictional movement between the powder material and the container. Venting the porous bed into a duct is sometimes necessary to exhaust any powder particles that might escape the container. This venting is usually designed to ensure a clean, safe working environment.

Fluidization

Every powder-coating material resin possesses its own peculiar fluidization characteristics. The amount of air required per cubic foot (m^3), density of the bed, and physical conditions at the top and bottom strata, all vary with the particular formula. In all cases, however, it is essential that the bed be completely aerated from top to bottom.

A layer of dead (dense or compacted) powder immediately above the porous membrane may lead to progressive stratification that ultimately affects the coating results achieved at the dipping sector. This concept is illustrated in Figure 5-4. For this reason, and

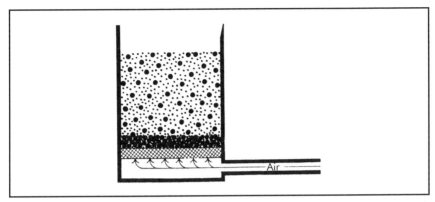

Figure 5-4. Fluidization—the "dead" powder at the bottom leads to stratification.

others, it is desirable to make powder additions to the bed in frequent, low-quantity increments to replace powder consumed on parts. A constant feed, conforming to production usage, is ideal, though not essential.

Bed Density

The density of a porous bed depends on the nature of the powder itself and the operating conditions. In many circumstances, it may be varied arbitrarily to produce desired results. However, in deep beds it can become a critical factor.

The density of a particular powder may be measured by its weight per volume. That measure is, however, not sufficient to determine how it will fluidize. The best way to evaluate density in an operating bed is to measure the percentage of expansion from the static to porous conditions. Correlating these data with previously determined standards indicates whether a particular powder will fluidize throughout the reservoir without requiring too much air or exhibiting sluggishness in the tank, as shown in Figure 5-5. This may be done simply by calibrating a small fluidizer to measure the percentage of expansion attained by a given amount of powder at the point of optimum fluidization.

Since all fluidizable powdered resins, thermosetting or thermoplastic, exhibit a particle-size distribution resembling a bell-shaped

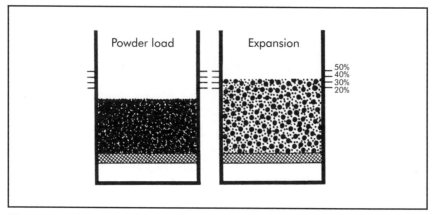

Figure 5-5. Powder load and expansion.

curve, it is significant that the bed's composition changes during operation. There is selectivity in deposition; the fines are removed from the bed at a higher rate than are the coarse particles.

ELECTROSTATIC FLUIDIZED-BED PROCESSES

Although the phrase "electrostatic fluidized bed" is used in describing this process, the "fluidized bed" portion of the system is of lesser importance in the actual powder deposition than it is in a dipping process. The electrostatic fluidized-bed process does not use a spray device or nozzle to apply the powder material to the parts.

In the electrostatic fluidized-bed process, the combination of the fluidized bed and electrostatic charging medium creates a cloud of charged powder particles above the powder bed. As in any fluidized bed, introducing compressed air through a porous membrane fluidizes the powder material. The depth of powder material in the bed is usually 0.50–1.00 in. (12.7–25.4 mm).

An electrostatic charging medium charges the air when high-voltage direct current (DC) potential is applied. Ionizing this air electrostatically charges the powder particles as the fluidizing air moves upward through the powder bed. The charged powder particles, having similar high electrical charges, thus repel each other and move upward. Aided by the fluidizing air, a cloud of charged powder forms above the upper surface of the powder bed. Grounded parts can be conveyed through or immersed into this cloud.

Basically, only the electrostatic field produced in the process is used to apply the powder material. In contrast to electrostatic spray methods, little air is used to control the volume and velocity of the powder material. Figure 5-6 illustrates this point.

Application

The electrostatic fluidized bed is ideally suited to substrates that have a relatively small vertical dimension, such as flat sheets, expanded metal, wire mesh, screen, wire, cable, tubing, and small parts on a conveyorized line. The electrostatic fluidized bed offers the advantage of being able to coat some objects, such as flat sheets, on one side only; the conventional fluidized bed requires dipping

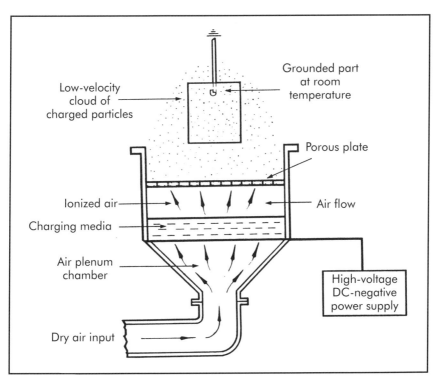

Figure 5-6. Electrostatic fluidized bed. (Courtesy Electrostatic Technology, Inc.)

of the entire part. The electrostatic fluidized bed includes an integral control panel and utilizes the same power-supply unit as the manual electrostatic spray system.

Preheating the part is not necessary in electrostatic fluidized-bed processes. The electrostatic forces—negative or positive to ground—cause deposition of the powder on either hot or cold surfaces. If the surface is hot, the deposited powder will sinter and adhere upon contact. If it is cold, the electrical charge on the particle will hold it in place until it is post-heated to cause flow. An advantage of post-heating is that powder can be selectively removed, reducing or eliminating the need for masking.

A common concern with all electrostatic deposition techniques is the *Faraday cage effect*, which can cause a poor powder build, especially inside acute angles. The electrostatic fluidized bed has been employed successfully in challenging applications such as coating the slots in motor armatures for insulation purposes.

Powder Characteristics

Factors affecting the application of powders in the electrostatic fluidized-bed process involve the types, sizes, and particle shapes of the powder material to be used. Generally speaking, the types of powders proven acceptable for the electrostatic fluidized bed process are:

- epoxy,
- epoxy/polyester hybrids,
- polypropylene,
- polyethylene,
- acrylic,
- polyester,
- nylon, and
- engineering thermoplastics such as perfluoroalkoxy (PFA), polyphenylene sulfide (PPS), polyether-ether-ketone (PEEK), and polyvinylidene fluoride (PVDF).

Fluidization and transfer efficiency also is influenced by the particle size distribution.

With the electrostatic fluidized bed, powder-particle-size classification (segregation) is not experienced to any great degree so long as deposition takes place near the upper surface of the bed. However, the further one moves above this point, the more pronounced the classification (segregation) becomes.

Equipment Characteristics

There are basically two styles of electrostatic fluidized beds, those with electrodes immersed in the powder bed and those with a remote charging media.

Locating the charging electrodes in the powder bed is effective, but it poses the hazard of arcing between the electrodes and the grounded substrate. The principal method for achieving powder charge is to locate the charging medium in a plenum below the powder bed, eliminating the possibility of arcing. Inlet air is ionized and the charge is passed to the powder during fluidization. The voltages employed with either method are nominally 30–100 kV. In most cases, negative polarity is used. Positive polarity may be of some benefit with nylon.

The amount of current from high-voltage sources used for electrostatic fluidized beds is about 200 microamperes. The current draw is independent of the amount of material being charged. It is related only to the proximity of the ground object to the charging media and to the resistive network used in the circuit. The amount of voltage applied to the charging medium affects the density of the charged powder cloud. The higher the voltage, the denser the cloud, and the greater the amount of deposited powder.

Other determining factors related to the amount of powder deposited are exposure time and the distance the product is above the upper surface of the aerated powder bed. It will be evident that the deposition rate lowers as the part is moved away from the charged powder.

Safety Considerations

Safety concerns vary, depending upon the design of the coating unit. The electrostatic fluidized bed design with the charging medium in the plenum is known to be a safe design, with no potential for an arc between the charging medium and a grounded part.

Safety must be carefully considered when using an electrostatic fluidized bed that has electrodes in the powder bed. Since the charged cloud density is extremely high, design of the high-voltage source is very important. The output voltage should be approximately 100 kV maximum and the maximum output energy (joules) when the unit is shorted to ground must not be greater than the ignition energy of the particular materials being applied. Also, output regulation of the supply—rate of fall of the output voltage with current draw increase—must allow rapid over-current protection.

An important consideration when using the exposed electrode bed with preheated parts is that the parts being coated must not be heated excessively in the preheat oven. When the parts being coated are too hot, gasses and vapors can be released within the bed, causing the air between the part and the electrode to become conducting, and creating a sparking condition between the part and source.

It is good practice to employ an exhaust system with the exposed-electrode-type bed. Top exhaust, entrance and exit port exhaust, or perimeter exhaust, are all appropriate techniques. The velocity of exhaust air should be a minimum of 50 ft/min (15.2 m/min). The same collection and recovery devices employed with electrostatic spray can be used with electrostatic fluidized beds.

Design and Application

Several electrostatic fluidized bed designs are available, but various patents may control some designs. All use the same basic concept of employing the fluidized portion as a material supply reservoir for the charged powder cloud. An arrangement typical of these devices is shown in Figure 5-7.

The plenum chamber, diffuser plate, and power chamber must all be made of an electrically insulating material. Normally, rigid polyvinyl chloride (PVC) or polyester-reinforced fiberglass is used for the plenum and powder chamber and either high-density porous polyethylene or porous ceramic for the diffuser plate. The supporting framework can be of steel construction.

The fluidizing air used in the process must be dry and free from such contaminants as oils, silicon, etc. Normally, air at a pressure

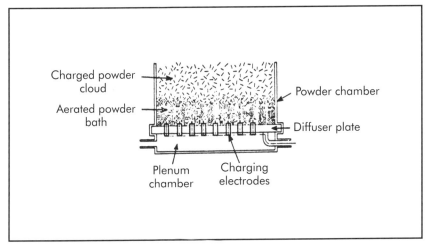

Charged powder cloud

Aerated powder bath

Powder chamber

Diffuser plate

Plenum chamber

Charging electrodes

Figure 5-7. An electrostatic fluidized bed design with electrodes in the powder bed.

of 2–10 psi will be required at a rate of approximately 5 ft³/min per ft² (0.14 m³/min per 0.09 m²) of diffuser plate. A suitable air drier must be used in conjunction with the air source, either a compressor or blower.

The electrostatic fluidized bed is used for a variety of substrate types. This includes linear materials such as small parts, wire, cable, screen, and coil products such as steel. The electrostatic fluidized bed in a production environment is usually combined with other processing systems into an integrated powder-coating machine. An example of such a machine is illustrated in Figure 5-8.

The machine in Figure 5-8 is designed to coat motor armatures with an insulating film of epoxy. Parts are loaded onto a conveyor that rolls the armature forward through the system. This method of conveyance presents a consistent distance from the powder bed to the surface to be coated on the cylindrical part. As the part is coated at essentially room temperature, the powder can be selectively and automatically removed from surfaces not to be coated, eliminating the need for masking. To attain high throughput rates, induction heaters are used to quickly raise the temperature of the part. The part is then passed through a convection zone for cure completion, and finally air cooled.

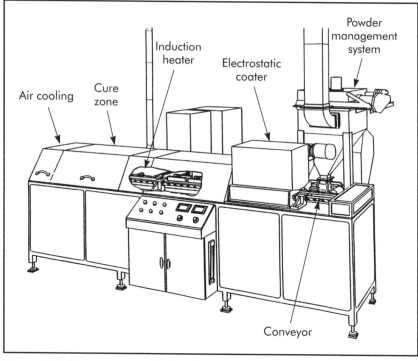

Figure 5-8. The electrostatic fluidized bed in a production environment is usually combined with other processing systems into an integrated powder-coating machine.

ELECTROSTATIC POWDER SPRAYING

Electrostatic spraying is the most widely used method of applying powder-coating materials. This process is the most efficient and effective means of applying powder coatings. To apply powder-coating materials with the electrostatic powder-spray process, five basic pieces of equipment are needed:

- powder feeder unit;
- electrostatic powder applicator;
- control module for powder applicator;
- powder spray booth, and
- powder recovery unit.

There are other devices to enhance the operation of these basic components.

In the operation of an electrostatic powder-spray system, powder is siphoned, or pumped, from a feeder unit through a powder-feed hose to the powder applicator(s). Powder applicators direct the powder in the form of a diffused cloud toward the part. Propelling force is provided both by air that transports powder from the feeder unit to the powder applicator, and by the electrostatic charge imparted to the powder at the applicator. Electrostatic voltage is supplied to the powder applicator by a source designed to transmit high-voltage, low-amperage electrical power to an electrode(s) attached to the powder applicator. As the diffused, electrostatically charged powder nears the grounded part, an electrical field of attraction is created, drawing the powder particles to the part and creating a layer of powder. Overspray—or powder not adhering to the part—is collected for reuse or disposal. In the powder recovery unit, powder is separated from the conveying airflow. Collected powder is then automatically or manually recycled back to the feeder unit to be resprayed. Air is passed through a filter media device into a clean-air plenum and then through a final, or absolute, filter back into the plant environment as clean air. The coated part is then carried from the application area and subjected to heat, which results in the flow out and curing of the powder material.

Advantages

The consistent finish characteristics and electrostatic "wraparound" realized in powder spray applications help reduce the need for highly skilled operators. In addition, there is no viscosity balance to maintain when coating with powder. Powder materials come "ready to spray" from the manufacturer.

No flash-off time is required with powder. The coated part can be transported directly from the spray area to the oven for curing. Reject rates can be reduced, as can costs involved in reworking rejected parts. Runs and sags are usually eliminated with the powder coating process. Insufficient or improper coating can be blown off the part (before heat curing) and the part recoated. This can eliminate the labor and costs involved in stripping, rehandling, recoating, and recuring rejected parts.

Users are finding that the powder spray coating process is easily automated. It can utilize automatic applicator movers, contouring mechanisms, robots, and stationary powder-applicator positioning.

Total production time can often be reduced, or production volume increased, with powder-spray coating.

Equipment

Most electrostatic powder-spray-coating systems are comprised of five basic pieces of equipment—the powder-feeder unit, electrostatic powder applicator, control module for the powder applicator, powder-spray booth, and powder-recovery unit. A discussion of each piece, its interactions with other components, and the various styles available is necessary to understand the functional operation of the process.

Powder-feeder Units

Powder is supplied to the powder applicator from the powder-feeder unit. Usually powder material stored in this unit is either fluidized or gravity-fed to a pumping device for transport to the powder applicator(s) (Figure 5-9). Units are also available so you can pump powder directly from the storage or shipping box.

The pumping device usually operates as a venturi, where compressed or forced airflow passes through the pump, creating a siphoning effect and drawing powder from the feed hopper into powder hoses or feed tubes, as shown in Figure 5-10. Air is generally used to separate powder particles for easier transporting and charging capabilities. The volume and velocity of the powder flow can be adjusted at the control module.

Venturi-style pumps have been developed to minimize the amount of powder surging from the applicator upon triggering. These are simple devices that allow compressed air to empty the powder hose when an applicator is de-triggered. They are generally used with automatic applicators.

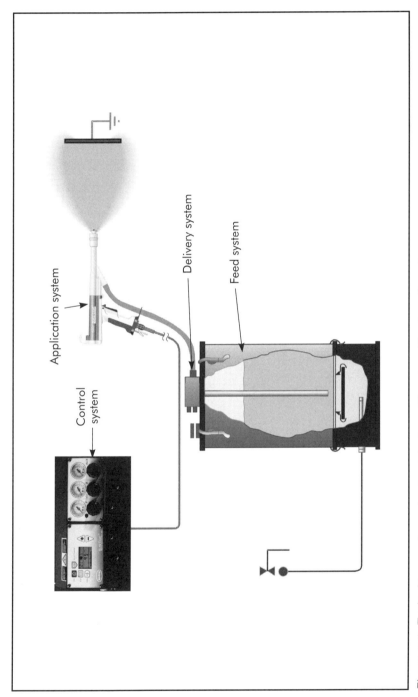

Figure 5-9. Typical types of powder-feed devices. (Courtesy Nordson Corp.)

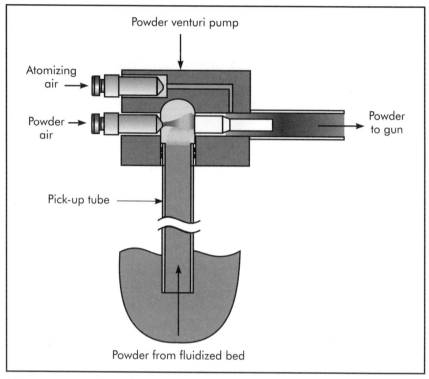

Figure 5-10. Typical Venturi pump. (Courtesy Nordson Corp.)

An auger-feed system is also available to provide more accurate and consistent powder flow than venturi-style pumps. The rotational speed of the auger is used to meter the amount of powder being delivered to the powder applicator. Auger systems are considerably more expensive than venturi-style pumps. The auger system can allow for a continuous flow of powder regardless of the applicator being triggered on or off.

In most cases, the feeder device utilizes air, vibration, or mechanical stirrers to aid in breaking up the powder mass. This action results in much easier transport of the powder, while assisting in regulating the volume and velocity of the powder flow to the powder applicator(s). Independent control of powder and air volumes aids in attaining the desired thickness of coating coverage. The powder feeder is capable of providing sufficient material to one or more electrostatic powder applicators several feet (m) away.

Powder feeders are available in many different sizes, with selection depending on the application, number of applicators needed, and volume of powder to be sprayed in a specified period of time. Generally constructed of sheet metal, the feeder unit can be mounted adjacent to or even be an integral part of the recovery unit.

Feeder units, which utilize fluidizing air to facilitate pumping of powder material to the powder applicator(s), are designed similar to fluidized beds. Compressed or forced air is supplied to an air plenum generally located at the bottom of the feeder unit. Between the air plenum and main body of the feeder unit is a membrane, usually made of a porous plastic-composite material. Compressed air passes through it into the main body of the feeder unit, where powder material is stored. The fluidizing action of the air results in lifting the powder material upward, creating an agitated or fluidized state (shown earlier in Figure 5-2). With this fluidizing action, it is possible to control the metering of powder siphoned from the feeder unit by an attached or submerged venturi-style pumping device (see Figures 5-9 and 5-10).

When gravity-feed-type feed units are used, the operation involves a conical or funnel-shaped unit in which powder material is stored. Pumping devices attached to this type of feeder unit usually are of a venturi-type pump (Figure 5-10). In some cases, vibration or mechanical stirrers are used to enhance powder siphoning by the venturi effect produced by the pumping device. Powder is gravity-fed to the pumping devices, and fluidizing of the powder is not necessary (Figure 5-9). Powder also may be delivered directly from powder boxes or containers using a double-well siphon tube, which provides enough local fluidization to allow uniform delivery.

Sieving devices are sometimes used in conjunction with feeder units to screen out any dirt, clumps of powder, and other debris, and to condition the powder prior to spraying. These sieves can be either mounted directly to or above the feeder unit to facilitate easier flow of powder within the closed loop of powder delivery, spray, and recovery (Figure 5-11).

Operation. Since the feeder is the first step in delivering powder to the part, it must be well set up and maintained. Poor operation at the feeder will result in noticeably deteriorated performance in the downstream equipment.

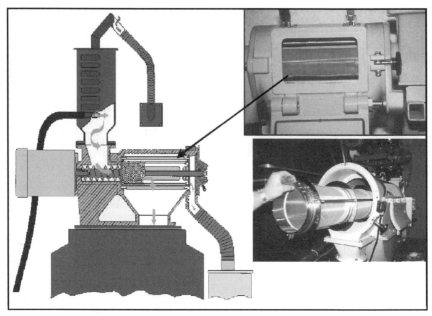

Figure 5-11. Rotary sieve. (Courtesy Nordson Corp.)

Air used to fluidize and pump the powder must be clean and dry. Oil, moisture, rust, and scale can contaminate the powder and even block the pores in the fluidizing plate. This in turn can lead to poor fluidization or even a ruptured plate.

The hopper must be properly vented to reduce pressure buildup. Poor venting can affect fluidization, and can cause fugitive powder to leak into the workplace, creating housekeeping and safety problems. The hopper also must be electrically grounded (earthed) to prevent static electricity buildup. In fact, the National Electric Code requires that all "dead" (not an active part of a circuit) metallic and conductive components in an electrostatic spray system be grounded. See National Fire Protection Association (NFPA) 33.

The feeder should be securely mounted or designed in a manner that effectively prevents it from tipping over and spilling powder into the workplace.

Pumping devices used to convey powder from the feeder to the powder applicator(s) should be inspected and cleaned on a regular basis. Parts exposed to high-velocity streams of powder are prone to wear and/or impact fusion. Worn parts result in loss of performance and control of the painting process. *Impact fusion* causes blockage and reduced flow rates. It is a sintering process in which the powder grains become fused together in hard, tightly bonded deposits on the walls of powder passages. The tendency to impact fuse is related to the velocity, directness of impact (blunt versus glancing impact), wall material, and the nature of the specific powder. A good preventive maintenance program is essential to proper operation of the system.

Sieving devices mounted on the feeder unit must be free of debris, and screens must be kept clear of powder buildup. Proper venting of the sieve is critical as the performance deteriorates if there is much differential pressure across the screen.

Powder Delivery Hoses

A key part of the powder's path on its way to the part being painted, the powder hose is often overlooked. Hose routing should be as direct as possible, with hoses trimmed to eliminate excess length. Routing should also avoid sharp bends or kinks. A bend radius of 9 in. (22.9 cm) is considered good practice and will help reduce wear, impact fusion, and pressure drop. Frequent inspection for internal wear, external chafing, and impact fusion is important.

A variety of material can be used in powder hoses, the choice being based on flexibility, kink resistance, freedom from *tribocharging* (static buildup due to powder flow), resistance to impact fusion, lack of chemical interaction with the powder, and wear resistance. Since there are many parameters to balance and many types of powders available, there is no "best" material.

The inside diameter will also have an impact on the volume and velocity of the powder being sprayed. Typically, smaller-diameter hoses are used in low-output applications where a reduced amount of powder is sprayed.

Applicators

Electrostatic powder applicators impart the electrostatic charge to powder particles, and shape and direct the pattern of those particles on the way to the part. The deposition of powder is controlled through variations in applicator position, velocity, shape of pattern devices, and electrostatic charge levels of the powder.

Powder applicators can be in the form of a spray gun, powder bell, or powder disk. Each applicator has different performance characteristics depending on the configuration of the part to be coated, production rates, and finish requirements.

Powder applicators are available in both manual (handheld) and automatic (fixed mount) types, in internal- and external-corona charging with internal or external high-voltage supplies, and in triboelectric (friction charging) types. All of these variations have their own benefits and weaknesses, and their own role in the charging of the powder.

Operating conditions. For electrostatic powder applicators to function properly and safely, the following conditions should be maintained.

- Powder applicators must be adequately grounded at their points of support to reduce the possibility of static charge buildup and the discharge of this static charge to a part or component in the spray area.
- Manual powder applicator operators must be adequately grounded (usually through the applicator handle) to prevent buildup of a static charge on their bodies during spray operations.
- Powder applicator parts that come into physical contact with moving powder must be inspected and cleaned on a regular basis. Parts contacting moving powder are prone to wear (if the powder material is abrasive) at high velocity and impact fusion. Worn parts result in poor control of powder flow, accentuated impact fusion, and require more frequent cleaning. If a part is obviously worn, it should be replaced.
- Electrostatic powder applicators (manual and automatic) should be checked periodically to determine the level of electrostatic charge being imparted to the powder material. The lack of, or decrease in, expected electrostatic charge indicates a problem in the electrostatic system and should be corrected as soon as possible. To reduce the possibility of electrical shock, troubleshooting guides should be utilized when inspecting or repairing any component within the electrostatic system.

- With fixed or automatic powder applicators, interlocks should be used to rapidly de-energize the high-voltage elements under any of the following conditions: stoppage of ventilating fans or failure of ventilating equipment from any cause, stoppage of conveyor carrying goods through the high-voltage field of electrostatic spray, and other conditions as prescribed by regulatory agencies.
- The electrostatic power unit must be adequately grounded.
- Electrostatic power units must be installed in a manner consistent with conditions specified by regulatory agencies.
- Electrostatic power units should be inspected periodically to determine the level of electrostatic kilovoltage output.
- Troubleshooting guides provided by the manufacturer should be strictly followed to reduce the possibility of electric shock.

Internal and external charging applicators. In these applicators, powder is charged by ion bombardment in a region close to the charging electrode. A high voltage of 30–100 kV and usually negative polarity are applied to the charging electrode. This voltage creates a very strong electric field around the electrode, which in turn causes a breakdown (ionization) of the surrounding air to form a corona discharge and an ion current. The ions are directed by the field to the powder particles, which are bombarded by the ions, transferring charge to the particles. The charged particles are then carried to the parts primarily by air currents and, to a lesser degree, by the electric field forces. Once the charged particles come close enough to the part (within about 0.4 in. [1 cm]) the attraction between the charged particle and the grounded part causes the particles to effectively deposit on the part (Figure 5-12).

Regardless of the type of applicator being used, the transport of well-charged particles to within 0.4 in. (1 cm) of the surface is essential for efficient and effective painting.

The external corona applicator is by far the most common type in use today, and is well suited for flatware and high line speeds with good uniformity and high transfer efficiency.

Performance on Faraday cage (cavity) areas has improved over the years with attention to careful pattern control and applicator placement. The more effective flat spray pattern is now used by

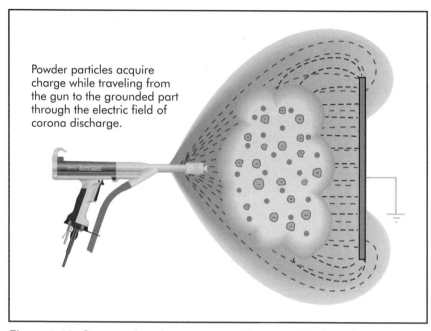

Powder particles acquire charge while traveling from the gun to the grounded part through the electric field of corona discharge.

Figure 5-12. Corona charging process. (Courtesy Nordson Corp.)

approximately 80% of all automatic applicators used to penetrate recessed areas. Since performance on Faraday cage areas depends on getting powder into the cavity, success is ultimately determined by pattern control and aerodynamics—the transportation means, rather than concentration on the electrostatic effects. The older conventional wisdom of turning the applicator voltage down to help penetrate a Faraday cage is ultimately counterproductive since the powder will be less well charged and less able to deposit on the part if it does succeed in getting into the cavity. Keeping the voltage as high as possible and working on the aerodynamic aspects of the transportation maintains a higher charge level on the powder and results in more efficient and effective coating of the cavity. Other developments to improve penetration into Faraday cage areas include counter electrodes. The counter electrode is a device designed to draw the lines of electrostatic force away from the recesses on complex parts, allowing the aerodynamics of powder spray to gain penetration into the Faraday cage area. A side benefit of this device can be a smoother overall finish by reducing the effects of orange peel.

In general, the rate or thickness of deposition is controlled by powder flow rate, position of the powder applicator, pattern used, velocity of the powder stream, line speed, part geometry, and the level of charge on the particles. Characteristics of the powder being sprayed can also affect deposition. Important factors are type of material, mean size, and probably most importantly, shape of the distribution curve.

In an internal-charge corona applicator, charging takes place by ion bombardment, the same as in an external-charge applicator. However, while the charging electrode is referenced to the grounded part to form the corona in an external applicator, the internal-charge applicator carries its own ground reference internally. The results of this are little or no external field forces, and little or no excess ion current. The reduced field will help penetrate the Faraday cage (cavity) areas since the external field provides a small diverting force that tends to move particles away from the cavity. Transporting powder into the cavity is almost entirely an aerodynamic process. The reduced ion current diminishes the tendency toward back ionization, which leads to smoother surface finishes with fewer "cratering" or "starring" defects. Reduction of back ionization also reduces the self-limiting effects of electrostatic powder coating and allows heavier film builds in the 10–15 mil (254–381 mm) range, which is difficult to achieve in external charge systems.

Internal-charging corona applicators tend to require more frequent maintenance than other types owing to the necessity of keeping their ground reference clean and free of powder, and because of their complex and often fragile components.

Triboelectric-charging applicators. Triboelectric applicators have no high-voltage power supply. They work by arranging the internal geometry so that air, when conveyed, rubs powder grains on the walls of the applicator, transferring charge by frictional means. The polarity of the charge is almost always positive. If triboelectric applicators are used with corona applicators, the corona applicators should be obtained in positive polarity as well (Figure 5-13).

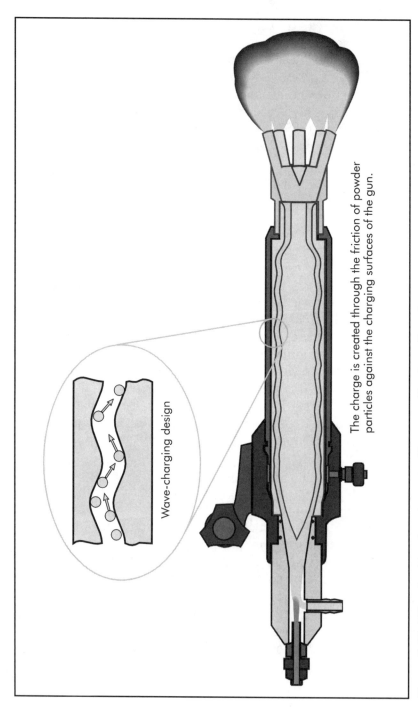

The charge is created through the friction of powder particles against the charging surfaces of the gun.

Wave-charging design

Figure 5-13. Triboelectric-charging gun. (Courtesy Nordson Corp.)

Generally, deposition rates are lower for triboelectric applicators, thus requiring more applicators per line. However, some of the better designs can achieve flow rates and charge levels comparable to external-corona-charging applicators, given a favorable powder. Since the charging process depends on inertial forces bringing the particles in contact with the walls, and since the charge transfer is related to the relative chemical compatibility of the powder and the wall material, the process is sensitive to both the particle size distribution and chemistry of the powder being sprayed. Some powders cannot be sprayed via triboelectric charging—for example, some metallic dry blends. Also many colors may not work unless specifically formulated for triboelectric-charging application. It is imperative that the user coordinates with his or her coating supplier when triboelectric applicators are used.

Triboelectric applicators are sensitive to environmental conditions. Dry compressed air (below 38° F [3° C] dew point) is a necessity when using this equipment. Furthermore, the environment where the powder is sprayed (the powder application room) should have a controlled heating, ventilation, and air conditioning (HVAC) system to ensure that the humidity in the room is within the manufacturer's guidelines (typically below 50% relative humidity).

Since there is no external electric field and no excess ion current, the triboelectric applicator has all the benefits associated with internal-charging-corona applicators, but without their stringent maintenance requirements and internal complexity.

Internal versus external power supplies. In corona-charging applicators (either internal or external charging), the high-voltage power supply may be located either internally or externally. There are tradeoffs inherent in both designs.

The internal supply receives low-voltage power from an external control unit through a thin, flexible, lightweight cable. The internal generator steps this low voltage up to the required 30–100 kV in the applicator. In an external supply, the high voltage is generated externally and carried to the applicator in a thicker, stiffer, heavier high-voltage cable.

Placing the generator in the applicator has benefits with regard to the cable, but adds weight to the applicator, and—in manual applicators particularly—places restrictions on the designer to keep the high-voltage generator light and compact. In applications where collisions with parts or machinery can occur, or in high-temperature environments, there is potential damage to a high-cost component if the generator is in the applicator. Conversely, the external supply has no practical restrictions on size or weight and it is protected from damage. Skilled design engineers can make both systems deliver equal performance in painting parts.

APPLICATION FACTORS

In addition to proper selection and set up of feeders, pumps, hoses, and powder applicators, a number of other factors can affect the end result. Foremost is the role of the powder itself, especially the powder's particle-size distribution.

Accumulated anecdotal evidence and experience indicate that the shape of the distribution curve, rather than the particle size, is the best indicator. A histogram of the particle-size distribution should show a narrow peaked shape. Broad, flat distributions with large percentages of both coarse and fine particles will show a number of undesirable properties, including poor fluidization, lower transfer efficiencies, and rapid buildup of fines. It is believed that the presence of coarse particles inhibits effective charging of finer particles. Where smoother, high-gloss finishes are desired, finer-grind powders are often required. However, it is important that not only the mean size, but also the shape of the distribution curve, be adjusted.

In tribocharging applicators, the powder plays a critical role in the operation of the applicator. While dry-blend additives can enhance tribocharging, best practice is to alter the melt mix to achieve a homogeneous material. In the past, conductivity was thought to be an indicator of chargeability in powders. Today, there is no evidence that this is the case.

The tendency of powder coating to limit the film build and promote more uniform coverage has been shown by John Hughes of the University of Southampton, England to be caused by back emission of ions from the deposited film. These ions act to discharge the incoming powder and prevent its deposition. Back ionization is also responsible for orange peel, cratering, and starring defects in the film. Back ionization can be overcome by moving the applicators further away, reducing the voltage, using an internal-charge applicator (either triboelectric or corona), or by applying the powder in thin layers with 10–15 seconds relaxation time between applications. Powder chemistry and particle-size distribution are also involved.

It is true that the powder spray process is dependent on electrostatics, and without charged powder there is not a process. However, the powder spray process is only about 50% electrostatics. The other half depends on airflow to shape the patterns and transport charged powder to the parts.

Faraday cages are areas where there is, by definition, no electric field from an external source. Under close examination, it can be seen that the cavities referred to as Faraday cages are also zones where it is difficult to achieve airflow. These are difficult areas to get powder into for aerodynamic reasons. If you cannot blow powder into a space, that space cannot be coated. The older conventional wisdom of reducing the voltage to overcome a Faraday cage is actually treating the symptom, not the underlying disease.

"Wrap" is also spoken of as an electrostatic phenomenon. And to be sure, without charge there is no evidence of wrap. But it is not electrostatics that transports powder around to the back-edge-flat panel or the backside of a round tube; aerodynamic turbulence provides the transportation.

Managing booth airflow and selecting the correct nozzle or pattern shaping device, advantageous applicator placement, and pump settings all contribute equally to the electrostatic effects.

six

Powder-spray Booths
and Recovery Systems

Efficient recovery of oversprayed material is one of the most important aspects of an electrostatic powder-spray system. Of the amount of powder leaving a spray gun, 30–90% adheres to the part. Oversprayed material must be collected effectively for disposal or recycling, depending upon its economic value. Recycling powder overspray (reclaim) is the best way to achieve the high system efficiency that is characteristic of the powder-coating process.

Air movement is the primary tool in virtually all methods of collecting oversprayed powder materials. Collection systems must address several important requirements:

- containment of overspray to limit worker exposure and minimize housekeeping;
- efficient separation of powder from air volumes;
- ease and time of color change;
- control of air movement in spray zones for augmentation of application transfer efficiencies;
- minimization of operational-noise levels for worker protection;
- adherence to safety and insurance agency regulations, particularly in the areas of fire and explosion prevention;
- ease and time of installation; and
- comfort and convenience for the worker during system operation.

Recovery systems can be as simple or as sophisticated as required by an application (Figures 6-1 and 6-2). A proper design, based on a sound understanding of applicable physics and engineering

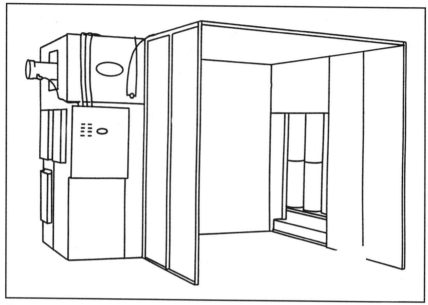

Figure 6-1. Batch booth with no quick color change.

fundamentals, is essential to the efficiency and longevity of the system's operation.

SPRAY BOOTHS

An important element of the spray booth is the material of which it is constructed. Typically, booths are made of polypropylene, polycarbonate, stainless steel, galvanized steel, coated-steel panels, or a sandwich wall of several plastic composites. Some booths are a combination of materials. One unique design utilizes retractable polyethylene sheeting. Material-selection criteria include:

- the material's effect on transfer efficiency (whether the booth material is conductive or nonconductive);
- cleanability (how strongly the powder is attracted to the booth wall);
- visibility in the spray area (translucence of the material); and
- strength, durability, and repairability given the size of the booth and specifics of the application.

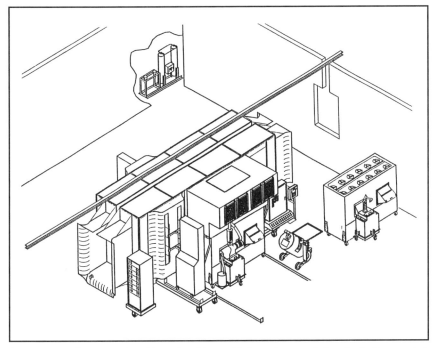

Figure 6-2. Conveyorized booth with multiple color modules that allow quick color change.

Spray booths can be designed for batch operations, conveyorized manual operations, or conveyorized automatic operations. Custom designs to meet unusual requirements are also available.

Parts openings in a spray booth should be sized properly to allow clearance for the largest part to be coated. Openings for automatic- and manual-spray stations should have sufficient access and be properly positioned for the best coating efficiencies. Accommodations must be made for induced airflow associated with spray equipment. Booth walls around part openings should be configured and contoured appropriately to minimize dead zones in the spray area where powder can build up.

Gravity-assisted Booths with Cyclone Recovery

Approximately 50% of oversprayed powder in a gravity-assisted booth with cyclone recovery will fall back to the feed hopper due to gravity. The balance is collected through an extraction duct to the reclaim system. The reclaim system consists of a virtually self-cleaning cyclone separator with reclaim recovery efficiencies up to 95%. The small fraction of powder remaining in the air stream from the cyclone is separated in a final filter before the air is returned to the powder-coating room. Figure 6-3 is only one of several possible configurations of this equipment. Typically, painted cold-rolled steel or stainless steel is used to construct the booth's cabin walls. The use of an efficient coating chamber with a self-cleaning cyclone allows an unlimited number of color changes without duplication of filtering equipment.

In gravity-assisted recovery booths, a portion of overspray returns by gravity directly to the feed hopper without entering the reclaim system. This minimizes the amount of reclaim powder generated by the system. This booth design lends itself to use with a variety of products such as facets, lawn-mower decks, housings, castings, etc. Products coated are usually arranged on a rack or hanger used in conjunction with an overhead conveyor.

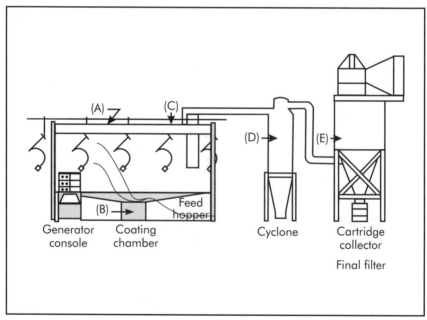

Figure 6-3. Basic components of an electrostatic-spray-coating system.

Quick-color-change Booth with Cyclone Recovery

A quick-color-change booth design replaces metal and/or rigid-plastic booth walls with thin plastic sheeting. When a color change is desired, pneumatic air motors index clean booth walls. This eliminates manually cleaning down the booth walls for a new color and allows the spray booth to change colors in one to two minutes. Once the new plastic is in place, operator openings and/or automatic gun slots are simply cut out where needed. This spray-booth style can be used with either a cyclone-reclaim system or a cartridge-module system. There are a variety of products used with this booth, including an overhead conveyor to transport the product through it.

Rigid Booth with Cyclone Recovery

In contrast to gravity-assisted booths, a rigid booth sends overspray through a cyclone-collection system as well as a detached powder-feed system. Otherwise, the recovery system operates like the gravity-assisted booth (Figure 6-4).

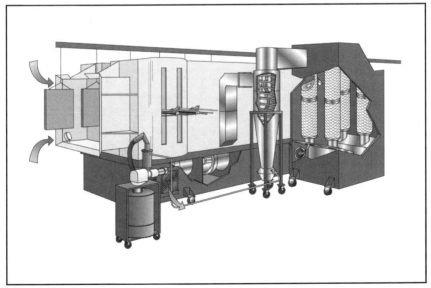

Figure 6-4. Cyclone booth. (Courtesy Nordson Corp.)

OTHER BOOTH TECHNOLOGIES

Horizontal Coating Booth

Typically, the horizontal coating booth is used to powder coat a product that requires coverage on all surfaces except one. The surface area to be masked is placed face down on the conductive conveyor belt, which transports the part through the spray booth, as wells as provides the necessary ground. The horizontal coating booth also serves as an automatic mask. When appropriate, this system helps to eliminate the cumbersome tasks of masking and racking. Parts may be manually or automatically loaded and unloaded, possibly through the use of a type of automatic vibratory feeder for loading (Figure 6-5). This booth design can be used with products such as disc-brake shoes, washers, nuts, etc.

A two-booth system is used for coating both sides of a product. The powder-coated surface is first melted or gelled before a de-

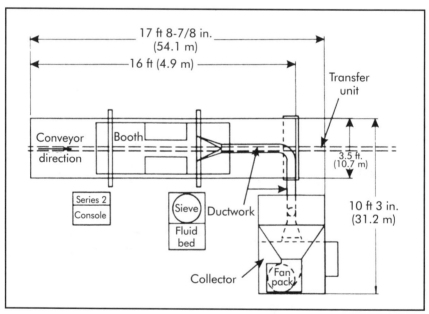

Figure 6-5. A horizontal coating booth can help eliminate the cumbersome tasks of masking and racking.

vice flips the product over to prepare for coating the other side in the second booth. This system is used in metal-blank and wood-sheet-coating systems.

Belt Booth

A belt booth employs a moving belt in the bottom of the booth (Figure 6-6). The belt is made of fabric and travels in a horizontal loop along the booth floor. Oversprayed powder is drawn to the belt surface by airflow created by the booth-exhaust system. A pickup head at the end of the booth vacuums off powder particles trapped on the belt surface. Once removed from the belt, powder is sent through the reclaim system to be separated from the vacuum airflow and prepared for reuse. Like other booths, a belt booth can be used with a variety of other equipment, including overhead conveyors.

Chain-on-edge Booth

A chain-on-edge booth uses cartridge filtration for powder recovery. It is used to coat products that pass through on a spindle or chain-on-edge conveyor. The conveyor for this booth is floor mounted and uses a pressurized shroud to keep powder off of the conveyor as the parts are coated. Types of products coated in a chain-on-edge booth are oil filters, motor housings, cans, bulbs, bottles, etc. Most of these parts are not complex in shape and can be rotated through the booth as they are coated.

Collector System

The powder collection system must maintain sufficient velocities through the booth openings to contain oversprayed powder. Accordingly, the size of the collection system is dictated primarily by the square footage (m^2) of the booth opening. Systems for collecting, separating, and processing oversprayed powder typically incorporate one or more of several techniques. Two types of cartridge-spray booths are utilized, depending on the size of the part being coated and the number of guns.

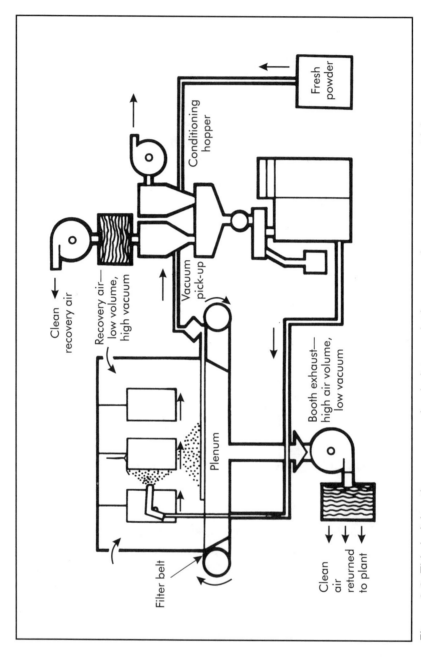

Figure 6-6. This belt booth uses a moving belt to assist in recovering overspray material.

Self-contained Booth

One type of application system is a self-contained spray booth and collector. Air used to contain and recover oversprayed powder is filtered through primary and final filters and returned to the plant as clean air. Solid-state controls for filter cleaning and powder recycling provide fully automatic, reliable operation.

The downdraft design of the booth locates the filter/collector module directly below the spray booth for maximum operating efficiency in most coating applications. The downward airflow allows oversprayed powder to naturally wash down over the part, resulting in more consistently uniform coating and improved operating efficiency. The downdraft design also allows more efficient use of floor space and access to either side of the booth for automatic/manual-spray-gun stations. The collector module is easily removed to facilitate cleaning and maintenance and ensure fast, easy color change.

Side-draft Spray Booth

In a side-draft spray booth/collector (Figure 6-7), the powder-spray booth provides clean, efficient, and flexible operation in manual- or automatic-powder-coating applications. Utilizing cartridge-filter technology, it provides high material utilization and fast color-change capability in a space-efficient and economical system.

The side-draft booth has a rollaway filter/collector module design. High-efficiency cartridge filters use reverse-pulsed air to prevent excessive powder buildup and extend cartridge life. With improved filter cleaning, the module provides maximum airflow throughout the coating operation for optimum system performance. The collector module's quick-disconnect feature ensures easy access to facilitate cleaning and color-changing operations.

A level-sensing device in the external feed hopper automatically controls flow of recovered overspray from the collector back to the feed hopper on demand. This improves fluidization of powder material and ensures optimum coating performance.

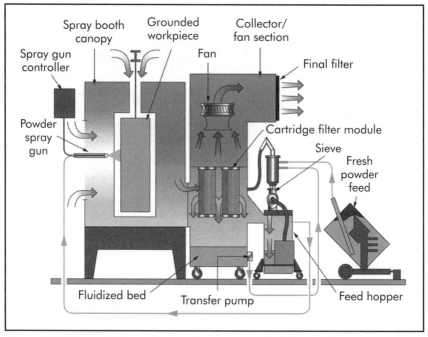

Figure 6-7. The efficient side-draft spray booth delivers high material utilization and fast color change. (Courtesy Nordson Corp.)

Open-collector-cartridge Filtration

Open-collector-cartridge filtration is the most common and efficient overspray-recovery method used in powder-coating applications. The open-face design of the collection unit eliminates the need for explosion venting (Figure 6-8). Powder is separated from an air stream and drawn through a cylindrical filter element. The powder is then removed from the filter element by a reverse-air, jet-pulse mechanism. The powder ejected from the surface of the filter falls into a collection zone and is then processed for return to the spray equipment. The air drawn through the cartridge filters passes through a secondary high-efficiency filter to remove any fine powder particles before it is returned to the work environment. Efficiency of the cartridge filtration is a function of several key design elements.

For efficient cleaning with minimal waste, the filter cartridge should be designed for a maximum effective surface area. The

Figure 6-8. The open collector is so named because of its open-face design, which eliminates the need for explosion venting. (Courtesy Nordson Corp.)

traditional air-to-cloth ratio associated with bag filters is not an appropriate measure for pleated-filter elements. Depending on the quality of the design, some portion of a tightly pleated surface area may not be accessible in the actual operation. Some filters are enclosed in a perforated metal screen to protect delicate paper media. This, however, can also reduce the effective surface area. With new high-strength-polyester media, an open-pleat design and the elimination of an outer screen are now feasible design elements (Figure 6-9).

Filter efficiency, as measured for a given powder-particle size, and the static-pressure drop across a filter are the two important measures of potential filter performance. Powder formulation and media composition also must be considered.

Reverse-jet-cleaning Mechanism

A reverse-jet filter cartridge cleans as a function of the rate of pressure buildup inside a cartridge element. A jet of compressed air that fills the cartridge interior while sealing the cartridge opening reduces this build-up. A well-designed cleaning mechanism is essential to the correct operation of a filter-cartridge-collection system (Figure 6-9).

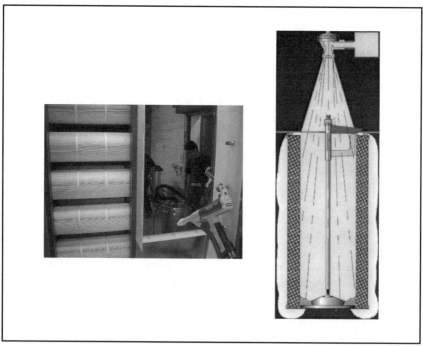

Figure 6-9. Filter cartridges. (Courtesy Nordson Corp.)

Collector-inlet Design

Appropriate inlet design includes baffling for turbulence reduction and distribution of the powder-laden air throughout the filter-element population. This is important to assure minimal disruption of the spray region and full utilization of filter media.

Cartridge-mounting Arrangement

The best design for mounting filters minimizes the number of surfaces to seal. It also maximizes utilization of the filter media. The most common cartridge arrangement is vertically hung filters, either single or double stacked, in a side-draft module (as shown in Figure 6-7). This arrangement minimizes re-entrapment of powder on collateral filters following pulse cleaning. The side location helps reduce the height requirement of the booth floor. Cartridges also can be mounted horizontally (usually in stacks of two), either in a side-draft module (Figure 6-10) or in a downdraft arrangement (Figure 6-11). When filters are mounted horizontally in the side-draft module, sometimes the filter stacks are staggered to reduce the tendency for powder to be recaptured on a lower set of filters once released from an upper-filter stack.

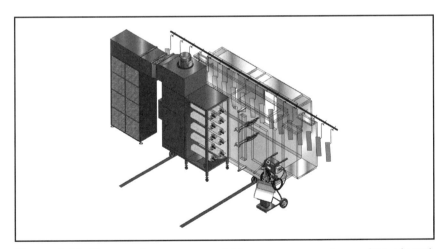

Figure 6-10. The most common cartridge arrangement consists of vertically hung filters, either single or double stacked, in a side-draft module. (Courtesy Nordson Corp.)

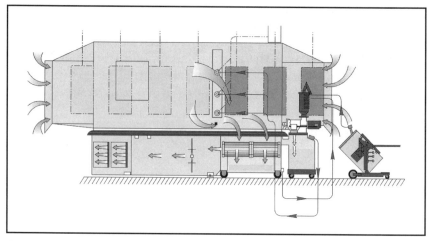

Figure 6-11. Cartridges can be mounted horizontally either below the spray area in a downdraft arrangement or in a side-draft module.

COLOR-CHANGE CONSIDERATIONS

Color change in a powder system requires that maintenance activities be performed on certain types of equipment. Guns should be blown out using compressed air and, in some cases, they should require disassembly. Feed hose should be blown out or, in extreme color changes, replaced. Pumps or injector blocks should be cleaned with compressed air. Booth walls must be cleaned, typically with a squeegee, by carefully wiping them down with the booth exhaust air in operation.

Color-change speed may depend upon the versatility of the re-claim system. Duplicate hoppers and sieves may be necessary to complete quick color changes.

When time is not a factor or multiple booths are used, solitary reclaims are satisfactory, but all areas contacting the powder must be vacuumed or wiped.

One early drawback to powder coating was the time required for changing colors. However, equipment suppliers have made various design improvements to all aspects of the powder coating system to minimize color-change time. One approach is a duplicate powder coating line. When it is time to change colors, the system containing the current color is rolled off line, while the system with the next color is positioned on line. This allows the system in the off-line position to be cleaned in anticipation of any additional colors. The number of duplicate powder coating systems required is dependent on how many colors are sprayed and the frequency of color changes. Color change within a single powder coating system can be accomplished in minutes.

Color changing a single powder coating system requires that three areas be considered. First, the application equipment (generally consisting of applicators, powder hoses, injectors, and the feed hopper) must be either cleaned or changed. Systems are available that automatically clean the automatic applicator on the inside and the outside. These systems also clean pick-up tubes, powder pumps, and hoses in a stand-alone containment system. This still involves the use of compressed air, but the process has been automated and is controlled through a programmable logic controller (PLC) (Figure 6-12).

Second, cleaning the spray-booth interior is necessary to prevent any cross contamination of the various powder colors. Caution should be exercised if compressed air is used. Air-blown powder may overcome the booth face velocity and migrate outside the spray booth. A rubber squeegee or damp cloth may be more desirable for the booth cleaning.

Finally, the recovery system must be prepared for the next color. The procedure for preparing the recovery system varies, depending on the style of the system.

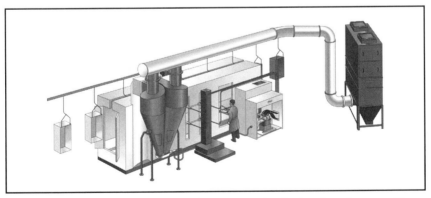

Figure 6-12. Automatic self-cleaning system for fast color change. (Courtesy Nordson Corp.)

seven

Powder Coating
System Design Considerations

A proper powder-coating facility is an important part of producing consistently high-quality products. Being able to design a
facility from the ground up is the ideal situation. Many systems,
however, must be installed within available plant space.

LOCATION

In every locality, guidelines and parameters exist for air quality
and liquid- and solid-waste disposal. This information should be
reviewed carefully with local regulatory agencies prior to designing a powder-coating system. Such discussions also may have a
bearing on site selection.

Factors inside and outside of a facility make the general location of an operation important. For example, even a properly designed powder-coating booth can have failures that result in the
accidental migration of powder to the environment. Consideration
should, therefore, be given to ambient in-plant operations that
could be affected by such a failure. Outside of a facility, it is important to consider if any neighbors' exhausts will be detrimental
to the powder-coating processing, and vice versa. A lumber mill
may not be the best neighbor for a powder coater, but probably
would be better than a cement plant. The same concept applies to
the location of equipment within the plant.

Using environmentally controlled rooms to isolate the powder
application and recovery process from the plant environment is
recommended when the plant atmosphere can adversely effect the

powder-coating process. Control of temperature and humidity within this room will ensure a high-quality finish on products processed through the line. In some geographic locations, this is necessary because of the ambient conditions of temperature and humidity. Powder, if exposed, readily picks up moisture and is temperature sensitive. Operations will be improved if conditions can be standardized. It is important to check with the powder supplier for other special considerations.

The following are considerations for choosing construction materials for an environmentally controlled room:

- Depending on the geographic location of the facility, the insulating properties of construction materials can save a great deal of energy.
- Construction materials can have a bearing on insurance rates for the building.
- Smooth interior wall surfaces are easier to maintain, thereby saving labor.

Migrating powder from a system (though not usually a problem in a well-designed system) can occasionally become troublesome. A small amount of powder can cover a large area if stray air currents pick it up. This powder accumulates over time on ledges and structural members. Enclosures with smooth walls and no catchall framework are easiest to maintain.

When designing an equipment layout for a powder operation, the location of all elements should be carefully analyzed. Overhead framing can be avoided at this stage. It is best if the exhaust from the booths and ovens is direct. Conveyors are most easily mounted when they are positioned relative to adequate building structures.

The relationship between the framing and the exhaust from equipment is often overlooked. While some buildings have a sufficient load factor to support conveyors built into the framing, others may not. Investigate the load factor before suspending anything from the framing.

The location of windows and doors in relation to spray booths and ovens is of great importance. Spray booths are designed to keep powder within a booth and provide uniform airflow as needed to transport the powder. A door or window opened next to, or in the vicinity of, a booth may completely disturb the booth airflow and cause difficulty. Disturbance of airflow can cause powders to leave the booth, distort the spray pattern, and draw outside dust onto the coating. Check with the equipment supplier on these points.

UTILITIES

Adequate consideration should be given to the availability and accessibility of all utilities. Energy is needed in a powder system to heat solutions and cure the applied powder. Water is needed in the metal preparation stages. Disposal facilities must economically handle the spent solutions and solids that are residual to the system. Consultations offered by local utility and sanitation people should be utilized. It is vital to be aware of their services and make them aware of needs.

OPERATION

Components of a powder-coating system rely on each other to maintain a safe and healthy operation. Proper operation of each component ensures a safe and healthy working environment and results in maximum productivity. Several factors should be considered in operating and maintaining a powder-coating system.

System Cleanliness

Powder introduced into a system should be as clean as possible and free of debris, moisture, oil, or other contaminants. Any contaminant in the powder will land on the part, resulting in either rejection or rework. Also, the contaminant will be distributed throughout the system, contaminating otherwise clean material. Further, a contaminant can cause blockage, or *blind* the filter media, reducing airflow through the system. Substantial reduction of airflow creates an unhealthy and unsafe atmosphere. The powder-containment capacity of the booth is reduced and powder is allowed to drift out into the work area. As airflow decreases through a spray booth, the minimum explosion concentration of the powder being sprayed can exceed safe limits. (Most systems are designed with interlocks that disengage or shut a system down when airflow decreases to an unsafe or unhealthy level.)

Gages are normally provided with most powder-coating systems. They indicate pressures across the face of the filter media and in the clean-air plenum of the filtered air returning to the work area. For safe operation of the system, gages should be checked daily and, if possible, logged for reference. Air provided for a system should be clean, dry, and oil-free. Refrigerated air dryers will remove moisture from the air and should be included in any powder installation. Oil-removal filters should be installed in the system's main air-supply line and checked or drained daily. The actual requirements for cleanliness and dryness of the compressed-air supply are available from the powder application and recovery supplier.

Another point to consider in maintaining cleanliness is the delivery and recovery equipment involved. To provide maximum efficiency, applicators, pumps, hoses, feed hoppers, distribution hoppers, and any surface that powder encounters should be checked for cleanliness. Powder lumps, impact fusion, debris, and worn powder-contact parts can block powder flow. Properly cleaned powder-contact parts are best for controlling powder flow to and from spray guns. Parts not properly cleaned increase impact fusing and part wear. One note of caution: never clean powder-contact parts with sharp or abrasive tools. A nick or scratch greatly enhances powder buildup on the part.

It is equally important to provide clean parts, hooks, racks, and conveyors. This enhances the electrostatic effect by ensuring a properly grounded part, and contributes to safe operation.

System Components

Proper design and construction are the first steps toward a successful and profitable powder-coating system. Each system is unique in design and application. Specifications that the user provides to the equipment suppliers determine the system's design. Information should always include all part dimensions, line speeds, film-build requirements, types of hooks or racks to be used, conveyor heights, dimensions of the space provided for system installation, production schedules based on batch sizes and number of colors involved, and projected production requirements. Information concerning the type of metal preparation and curing facilities also should be provided. This enables the equipment supplier to design a system to exact specifications.

During the first few weeks of operation, a system should be monitored closely to determine its particular operating characteristics. These observations can be used to establish operating procedures for each product conveyed through the system. Remember, the system design should be based on the largest part that will be coated and finished. Smaller parts may require adjusting the number of applicators used, powder flow, electrostatic setting, proximity of the applicator to the part, or any combination of these variances. By knowing in advance the precise settings and making these adjustments, excessive powder usage can be avoided and the desired efficiencies will be achieved.

Daily, weekly, and monthly preventive and corrective maintenance procedures should be established. If this is done, the efficiencies necessary to justify operation are easily attained. Some hints for maintaining system efficiencies are:

- Check oil and dirt-removal filters installed in air lines on a regular basis. Drain filters often and replace when necessary.
- Check the operation of the refrigerated air dryer at least once a week. Just because the air dryer is running, it does not mean it is operating properly. Gages will indicate the inlet and outlet temperatures of compressed air.
- Check powder-contact parts periodically for wear. If the parts show excessive wear, replace them. Failure to do so will result in more time spent on cleaning the part to remove impact fusion and affect the system's operation. Never use sharp objects to clean parts. Always maintain a reasonable supply of spare parts.
- Check all ground connections on a regular basis. The loss of ground could affect the transfer efficiency of the spray guns. A hazardous situation could be created if the ground between the workpiece and hanger is lost. Strip hangers on a regular basis. Grounding must be below one mega ohm to ensure a safe and reliable coating process.

- Check for pressure drops across the filter media. A reduction in airflow through the booth could result in poor powder containment. An unsafe situation could be created if the minimum explosion concentration exceeds safe limits. Clean absolute filters on a regular basis. If absolute or final filters require frequent cleaning, this could be an indication of a ruptured or leaking primary filter media, which should be checked and replaced if necessary.
- Clean the booth daily with a squeegee or other grounded nonsparking device. Never use rags or paper towels to clean a booth area. Lint could contaminate powder material and create finish problems. More extensive cleaning should be performed on a weekly or biweekly basis.
- Clean powder-spray guns and feed pumps daily. Use an air hose to blow powder from the hoses, pumps, and guns. Visual inspection will reveal the need for additional cleaning or parts replacement. Be sure there are no loose hose connections between pumps and guns. All air-line fittings should be secure. Locate feed hoppers as close to guns as possible to reduce hose length and the possibility for kinks or bends.
- Post the maintenance procedures in areas where operators and supervisors will see them. Provide check-off lists for maintenance procedures.

Health Hazards

Some materials contained in powder coatings may pose health hazards to personnel within the immediate spray area. Pigments, curing agents, polymers, and fillers all present potential health hazards if permitted to escape the spray-containment area. Improper ventilation or improper handling and use of powder can cause such hazards. Occupational Safety and Health Adminstration (OSHA) regulations govern the handling and use of powder-coating materials. A Material Safety Data Sheet must be provided by the supplier, advising the user of any hazards associated with the powder-coating material and precautions concerning skin contamination and respiratory exposure.

The following recommendations should be considered to reduce potential health hazards associated with powder-coating materials.

- All workers who handle powder material should wear gloves and masks. Gloves and masks are needed when opening fresh material containers, dumping material into supply hoppers, cleaning or performing maintenance on equipment, and/or disposing of empty material containers. Powder, when exposed to the skin for extended periods of time, can dry the skin. Only conductive gloves should be used when operating manual-spray equipment. This will ensure that the operator remains grounded when using these devices.
- Facilities should be provided for proper washing of skin exposed to powder materials. Soap and water are considered to be the safest and most effective means of cleansing skin exposed to powder. Personnel should be encouraged to wash with soap and water frequently. It is certainly necessary before eating, drinking, or performing other bodily functions. Skin reactions can occur in some powder-exposure cases and should be treated by frequent washing or seeking medical attention. Cleansing the skin with organic solvents is never encouraged.
- Exposure to respiratory inhalation should be prevented through the use of respirators or masks. Also, proper ventilation of the powder-spray system prevents respiratory inhalation. It also keeps the environment safe from explosions by minimizing the possibility of ignition from static-electrical sparks or other ignition sources. (National Fire Protection Association [NFPA] 33 specifies and establishes proper ventilation guidelines.) The safest operating procedures specified for powder-spray applications are also the most productive.

The electrostatic powder-coating process is somewhat different from the more conventional means of applying product finishes such as wet spray. The electrostatic process applies electrically charged powder material to grounded parts. Powder adheres to the part by an electrostatic charge imparted to the powder during the spray process. To ensure attraction and transfer efficiency, two conditions must be met. First, the part being sprayed must be properly grounded. Second, the electrostatic spray equipment must be functioning properly. If either of these conditions is not met, the net result will be poor transfer efficiency and, in the case of a poorly grounded part, unsafe conditions.

Safety should always be incorporated into operating and maintenance procedures for the powder-coating system. These procedures should consider all aspects of an operation, including:

- storing and handling powder materials;
- spraying parts within the spray booth;
- conveying parts through the spray booth;
- cleaning and maintaining equipment;
- troubleshooting equipment;
- system startup and shutdown;
- reading, calibrating, and setting control gages and regulators;
- recording daily critical ventilation-pressure readings;
- responding to alarms, interlocks, and safety control devices; and
- disposal of waste materials.

Guidelines for safe operating procedures are provided by NFPA in several publications and have been incorporated into governing OSHA regulations. Reference guidelines can be found in:

- NFPA Bulletin 33;
- OSHA Section 1910.107, and
- NFPA Industrial Fire Hazards Handbook, Chapter 25.

Here are some highlights from these references.

First, equipment should be listed and approved by nationally recognized approval agencies, such as Underwriter Laboratories, Inc. (UL), Factory Mutual (FM) Engineering Corp., Edison Test Labs (ETL), and others in the United States. In Canada, certification by the Canadian Standards Association (CSA) is required. Approved status of the equipment means the equipment has been tested and evaluated by a nationally recognized approval agency and met the established standards of safety.

Spray operations must be confined to properly designed spray booths, spray rooms, or designated spray areas. All spray areas should be provided with mechanical ventilation adequate to transplant flammable or combustible dusts, vapors, mists, residues, or deposits to a safe location. Ventilation for the spray booth should be adequate to confine the air-suspended powder to the booth and recovery system at all times. Average air velocity through electrostatic-booth openings should not be less than 60 ft (18.2 m) per minute.

Parts being coated should be supported on conveyors or hangers properly connected to ground, with a resistance of 1 mega ohm or less. All electrically conductive objects in the spray area, except those objects required by the process to be at high voltage should be adequately grounded. Spray areas must be protected with an approved automatic fire extinguishing system. Fixed powder-application equipment should be protected further by approved flame detection apparatus that will, in the event of ignition, react to the presence of a flame within one-half second and:

- Shut down all energy supplies (electrical and compressed air) to conveyor, ventilation, application, transfer, and powder-collection equipment.
- Close segregation dampers in associated ductwork to interrupt airflow from application equipment to powder collectors.
- Activate an alarm.

eight

Heating

Heating operations are required for a variety of purposes on a powder-coating line. It is usually accomplished with ovens of various forms selected according to the needs of a particular operation. Ovens can heat parts such as porous castings to:

- rid them of occluded gas;
- burn accumulated material from part supports in a cleaning step;
- raise the temperature of previously cleaned parts to prepare them to accept powders, as in the fluidized-bed process; and
- reheat coated and cooled parts to promote further flow of the applied material.

Heating can remove water remaining from prior operations that would cause trouble if carried to the powder-coating station. Most importantly, heating is used to melt, flow, and cure powdered materials applied at room temperature by electrostatic-spray processes.

Since powder-coating operations are usually conducted at high speeds in a production environment, heating functions must be carried out in the most efficient and cost-effective manner. Requirements of a particular application must be thoroughly studied and matched with the capabilities and design principles of available ovens. Thoroughly investigating all aspects of the heating components of a powder finishing line is critical to achieving an efficient, effective, and satisfactory operation that will produce a high-quality product.

PREHEATING

Parts on their way to be coated are preheated when it is necessary to dry off any moisture remaining from previous cleaning or conditioning steps. Such heating must be just adequate enough to accomplish this simple function. Temperatures can be about 250° F (121° C) at most, and can be attained with any number of available ovens. Water vapor must be removed to allow a time-dryness relationship to occur.

Preheating is also needed to raise the temperature of parts to be coated by processes that fuse powder on the part. This requires the establishment of a temperature-time coating cycle, so coating thickness can be reproduced. The hotter the part, the more material that will adhere before the temperature falls below the fusion point. Heat can reduce the Faraday cage effect by allowing penetration into crevices that are otherwise hard to penetrate. The temperature-time curve for such ovens must be known and reproducible. Generally, such ovens need not be ventilated beyond the required safety considerations.

POST-HEATING

Post-heating operations on a powder finishing line are perhaps the most critical. They are used to melt, flow, and cure the powder applied to the part at ambient temperature, such as with the electrostatic-spraying process. The application of heat has to be very carefully controlled because temperature-fluidity characteristics of a particular powder are peculiar to that powder. It is this relationship that determines how the flow of material will take place as the temperature is raised. Most materials cross-link and become more viscous with time at a given temperature. For thermosetting materials, this process further complicates the control.

Final properties of the coating can be acquired uniformly over the part only if all areas of the coating are treated in thermally equivalent conditions. For this reason, post-heat ovens must be of high quality and equipped with adequate controls to ensure reproducibility.

PROCESS CONSIDERATIONS

Many variables must be considered and studied when selecting ovens for the powder-coating line. Of utmost importance are:

- part size, configuration, mass, material, and temperature limitations;
- conveyor method, part holder, and line speeds; and
- powder formulation type, thickness, cure profile, color, gloss, and test for cure.

All parameters should be defined and communicated to equipment and powder suppliers to ensure an integrated system and successful installation.

METHODS OF HEATING

Several individual and combinations of heating techniques have been successfully used to cure various powder coatings in a wide range of applications. New technology in curing ovens and powder coating has allowed dramatic improvements in cure results in the last few years.

Gas or Electric Convection

Convection heating uses air as a medium to transfer heat from the energy source to the product. Many convection systems use a fuel source (gas or oil) to provide heated-air circulation in the oven chamber. Using a combustion chamber, the oven atmosphere can contain combustable products, solvent vapors, and possibly traces of unburned fuel. Other convection ovens utilize electric elements to provide a clean, safe method of convection heating.

With convection heating, the time required to bring powder deposited on the part to its cure temperature largely depends on the mass of the part and the rate at which the part accepts heat. Large metal objects may require 30 minutes or more to reach the desired cure temperature. Smaller parts can be brought to the right temperature much more rapidly in 6–8 minutes. This heat absorption by the part, other than the surface, is a waste of heat energy as far as powder curing is concerned. Convection heating may be the most flexible and efficient method of curing, considering process requirements, such as part configuration.

Temperature-response time of large convection ovens is not particularly rapid, often taking an hour or more to reach the operating temperature from a cold start. Convection ovens require considerable floor space and routine cleaning, if good finishes at high-production rates are to be obtained. Despite these limitations, convection ovens are currently the most popular for industrial painting and curing. Energy and operating costs, however, are often high, and users should be aware of more cost-effective alternative methods.

Infrared Radiation

Infrared heating uses electric or gas energy to produce a direct, radiant method of heating. Infrared heat is transmitted directly from an emitter to the product via electromagnetic waves that travel at the speed of light. Unlike convection heating, high-intensity infrared requires no medium for heat transfer. Radiation is a line-of-sight method; it only cures what it sees. Heated energy is transferred quickly, cleanly, and efficiently. Short-wave heaters also penetrate the substrate. High-intensity infrared can have fast temperature-time response. Curing ovens using this method of radiation heating are compact in size and can be zoned to match the exact product configuration and size. Oven startup times of 1–15 minutes are common. With amenable part configurations, savings in energy, space, and time can be realized with infrared heating.

Infrared radiation is best used with products of consistent shape, and produced on dedicated lines with large volumes. A direct line of sight (heater-to-object surface) is needed for proper powder cure, and cure is affected by object distance. Rotating the coated product during the infrared cure for round or cylindrically shaped products provides uniform heating with consistent cure results. Reflow and cure times range from 1–12 seconds using high-intensity infrared; other infrared systems may require more time.

OVEN-CAVITY ATMOSPHERE

Oven-cavity atmosphere is critical to both safety and product appearance. Solvent or vapor concentration must be kept to not more than 25% of the lower-explosion limit (LEL). Thus, a specific amount of oven air may be exhausted and replaced on a continuous basis during operation. Fresh input air should be introduced to the oven for solvent or vapor dilution, and then exhausted. In powder applications, the amount of solvent released is near zero. Volatile substances may consist of low-molecular-weight resins, water, blocking agents, etc., but usually no solvents.

Exhausted air in all powder-curing applications is routed outside the building. Powders contain no hazardous solvents. The exhaust- and supply-air systems are arranged to provide a slightly negative pressure within the oven. Large convection ovens are often located near factory roofs because of the heat loss and flow to the work area around the oven.

Ovens must be sized to permit adequate cure of the powder and airflow. Wall construction of the oven cavity is often of steel. It is typically assembled from modules and insulated to contain heat within the oven.

SAFETY

The exhaust fan is a primary oven-safety feature. It removes solvents and combustion vapors to avoid explosion. Powder vapors must be removed to keep the powder from discoloring from the materials that come off during the curing process. Exhaust and recirculation fans must be equipped with airflow sensors. These devices will monitor serious disruptions in airflow and shut down the oven if any are detected.

Manufacturing-safety provisions and regulatory requirements should be followed for safe operation of ovens. All oven-safety features should be checked on a quarterly basis.

nine

Storage and Handling

Powder, like any coating material, must be shipped, inventoried, and handled in its journey from the powder-coating manufacturer to the point of application. Manufacturers' recommendations, procedures, and cautions should be followed. Although various powders may have specific requirements, some universal rules apply. It is important that powders always be protected from:

- excessive heat;
- humidity and water; and
- contamination with foreign materials, such as other powders, dust, dirt, etc.

These are so important they deserve more elaborate explanations.

EXCESSIVE HEAT

Powders must maintain their particle size to allow handling and application. Most thermosetting powders are formulated to withstand a certain amount of exposure to heat in transit and in storage. This will vary according to types and formulation, but can be estimated at 80–120° F (27–49° C) for short-term exposure. When these critical temperatures are exceeded for any length of time, one or all of the following physical changes may happen. The powder can sinter, pack, and/or clump in the container. Pressure of powder weighing on itself (for example, large tall containers) can accelerate packing and clumping of the powder toward the bottom of the container. Manufacturers recommend a long-term storage temperature of 70° F (21° C) or lower. Unless its exposure to heat has been excessive over an extended period of time, powder that has experienced such changes can usually be broken up and rejuvenated after being passed through a screening device.

Powders with very fast- or low-temperature-curing properties may undergo chemical changes as a result of exposure to excessive heat. These powders may partially react, or *B stage*. Even though they may be broken up, the same flow and appearance characteristics as unexposed powders can not be achieved. They will have, and irreversibly retain, restricted flow, even to the point of a dry texture. Powders formulated with chemical-blocking agents to prevent curing below certain trigger temperatures do not typically B stage at temperatures below 200° F (93° C).

HUMIDITY AND WATER

Water and powder do not mix when the intent is to spray as a dry powder. Exposure to excessive humidity can cause the powder to absorb either surface or bulk moisture. This causes poor handling, such as poor fluidization or gun feeding, which can lead to gun spitting and, eventually, feed-hose blockage. High moisture content will certainly cause erratic electrostatic behavior, which can result in changed or reduced transfer efficiency and, in extreme conditions, affect the appearance and performance of the baked coating film.

CONTAMINATION

Because powder coating is a dry process, contamination by dust or other powders cannot be removed by filtering, as it can with liquid paint. It is imperative, therefore, that all containers be closed and protected from grinding dusts, aerosol sprays, etc.

STORAGE RECOMMENDATIONS

The storage-stability properties of powder coatings need not cause problems at the end user's facility, provided that a few simple precautions are taken. Among these are:

- The control temperature should be 70° F (21° C) or less. Powder requires minimal storage space. For example, a semi-tractor-trailer-sized area can accommodate 40,000 lb (18,144 kg) of powder, which is approximately equal to 15,000 gallons (56,775 L) of liquid paint.
- Efficiently rotate the stored powder to minimize the amount of time it is kept in inventory. Powder should never be stored for a period exceeding the manufacturer's recommendation.
- Avoid having open packages of powder on the shop floor to preclude possible moisture absorption and contamination.
- Condition powder prior to spray application by providing preconditioning fluidization, as is available on some automatic systems, or by adding virgin powder through the reclaim system. These techniques will break up the powder if minor agglomeration has occurred in the package.
- Maximize powder-transfer efficiency in the booth to avoid problems associated with recycling large quantities of powder.
- Minimize the amount of powder coating material held on the shop floor if the temperature and humidity of application areas are not controlled. However, if powder coatings are stored in an environmentally controlled room, the powder should be moved to the spray area at least 24 hours before use to acclimatize it.

SAFETY

Powder coatings contain polymers, curing agents, pigments, and fillers that require safe handling procedures and conditions. Pigments may contain heavy metals, such as lead, mercury, cadmium, and chromium, although most powder coatings on the market today do not contain these materials. The handling of materials containing such elements is controlled by OSHA regulations. End use may be restricted according to Consumer Product Safety Commission Regulations.

Under some circumstances, OSHA regulations require the applicator to inform employees of the hazards associated with handling certain components or powder coatings. The applicator is advised to obtain this information from the supplier in the form of a Material Safety Data Sheet. Powder coatings should be handled in a manner that minimizes both skin contact and respiratory exposure consistent with particular Material Safety Data Sheet recommendations. Obvious health reactions attributed to any powder-coating exposure should be referred to a physician as soon as possible.

Opening, emptying, and handling powder containers, such as boxes and bags, often present the greatest worker exposure, even with well-designed systems. Engineering practices, personal protective equipment, and good personal hygiene should be used to limit exposure. In a well-designed spray operation, there should be negligible exposure of employees to dust. Powder coatings, because of their fine particle size and frequently large percentage of titanium oxide (TiO_2) will absorb moisture and oil readily.

If powder is left in contact with the skin for extended periods, it tends to dry out the skin. To prevent this, workers should wear conductive gloves and clean clothing. Operators of manual electrostatic applicators must be grounded. To prevent carrying powder away from work, workers should change clothes prior to leaving the workplace. If powder does get on the skin, it should be washed off at the earliest convenient time, at least at the end of the day. Workers who show skin reactions after exposure to powder must be especially careful to wash frequently. Washing the skin with organic solvents is an unsafe practice that should be forbidden. Generally, cleansing with soap and water is the appropriate hygienic practice. Additional information should be obtained from the supplier's Material Safety Data Sheet.

ten

Touch-up, Recoat, and Stripping

The methods of part repair after powder coating can be put into two categories—touch-up and recoat.

Touch-up repair is appropriate when a small area of the coated part is not covered and is unable to meet finishing specifications. When hanger marks are not acceptable, touch-up is required. Touch-up also may be used to repair slight damage from handling, machining, or welding during assembly. Touch-up is performed using a compatible liquid paint designed for spot application by the powder coating formulator.

Recoat is required when a part is rejected because of a large surface area defect or when touch-up is not acceptable. At this point, there are a variety of options that should be considered carefully. Usually the rejected part can be repaired with a second coat. Another option is stripping and repainting the part. Stripping can also clean part hangers to provide a good ground for electrostatic spray.

TOUCH-UP

Liquid touch-up paint is applied with a small brush, aerosol spray, or airless gun. The paint is air-dried. The drying process can be accelerated with a low-temperature bake. Touch-up paint is used after the powder coating has been fully cured in a bake oven. Hanger marks, light spots in corners and seams, damage from welding or assembly, and other small defects can be touched up. Generally, a color-matched acrylic enamel or lacquer is used. Touch-up paint cannot be used if it will not meet the performance specifications required during the expected life of that part. Touch-up should not be used to repair a faulty finish unless the resulting product meets inspection standards. Before use, the original powder coating formulator should approve all touch-up paints.

RECOAT

Applying a second coat of powder is the common approach to repair and reclaim rejected parts. However, the defect should be carefully analyzed and the source corrected before recoating. Do not recoat if the reject is caused from a fabrication defect, poor-quality substrate, poor cleaning or pretreatment, or when the thickness of two coats together will be out of tolerance. Also, if the part is rejected due to undercure, it merely needs to be rebaked at the required schedule.

A second coat is effective to cover light areas, surface defects from dirt and contamination, rough spots from heavy film build or gun spitting, and color change from severe overbake. Rough surfaces and protrusions should be sanded smooth before recoating.

Parts inspected on-line can be left on the conveyor to receive a second coat. These parts can pass through the pretreatment stages with raw parts. If the recoated parts show water spots or stains, an adjustment can be made in the final rinse stage. Chemical suppliers can offer recommendations. When parts for recoat are hung together, cleaning and pretreatment is not necessary. However, if the rejected parts have been stored to accumulate a practical number, they should be checked for dirt and contamination before recoating.

Coat Entire Part

The second coat should be applied to the entire part at the desired film thickness. A common mistake is to coat only the defect area. This leaves a rough gritty surface where there is only a very thin overspray layer of powder on the remainder of the part. The same recommended cure schedule should be used for the second coat.

Intercoat adhesion can be checked after recoating on selected samples by using the crosshatch test or simply scratching the surface to see if the second coat peels easily from the first. Some powder coatings may need to be lightly sanded to provide a good anchor for the second coat.

Rebake

When a part is undercured during the first coat, just returning it to the bake oven for a normal cure schedule at the specified time and temperature can repair it. Properties can be recovered when a part is properly cured, with some exceptions, such as when certain chemically controlled, low-gloss coatings are used. Partial curing will result in a higher gloss.

STRIPPING

Usually the last alternative for part repair, stripping rejected parts can add greatly to production costs, as well as disrupt the production-line flow. Stripping coated parts becomes necessary, however, when poor pretreatment or touch-up causes the coating to be unacceptable and, therefore, rejected.

On the other hand, stripping plays an important role in the effectiveness of a powder-coating line by resulting in clean hangers that provide good electrical grounding. Hangers should be stripped periodically.

Chemical Strippers

Chemical strippers can be used hot (raised temperature) or cold (ambient) in a dip tank. There are acid, alkaline, and molten-salt types, with selection dependent on the type of parts, the hangers, and the coating to be removed. The main advantage of chemical strippers is the low initial capital investment for equipment. Disadvantages include safety hazards related to handling the chemicals; the high costs of chemical replacement and disposal; and that the chemicals are laden with paint. Some parts, such as aluminum alloys, may not be able to withstand corrosion that can result from chemical strippers.

Burn-off Ovens

Burn-off, or *pyrolysis,* ovens are for stripping. They use high temperatures to incinerate the coating. Burn-off ovens can be batch-type or on-line ovens that operate at about 800° F (427° C), with the pollution-control exhaust operating at temperatures of approximately 1,200–1,300° F (649–704° C). Burn-off ovens eliminate pollution and disposal problems. They are relatively efficient to operate, but require a large capital investment and need some type of post-cleaning to remove residual ash. The parts must withstand 800° F (427° C) temperatures. Some coating chemistries are not suitable for this stripping technique. It is wise to consult with the equipment manufacturer and local regulatory agencies for more information. It also should be noted that repeated stripping of tooling might require that a resilient type of alloy be used to prevent breaking or deforming.

Shot Blasting

Shot blasting, or abrading, can be used to strip parts or hangers when other methods have been ruled out. This process is very slow, due to the toughness of the cured powder coating. The disadvantage of this process is that it erodes (thins) the tooling and exposes more surface area, which becomes harder to strip when recoated.

Cryogenic Stripping

Cryogenic stripping embrittles film with liquid nitrogen, and then uses a nonabrasive shot blast to easily remove the coating. This is a fast, nonpolluting method, but it requires specialized equipment. Parts must endure –100° F (–73° C) temperatures, and an alloy may need to be considered for tooling.

Stripping Cured Coatings

Stripping is an important function of any modern organic finishing operation, and is often the most antiquated link in the overall coatings process. Whether for the salvage of rejected coated components, or as part of routine line maintenance, stripping of cured coatings has an important impact on overall line quality and economy.

When evaluating the stripping of a rejected coated part, the first question to ask is whether the component is valuable enough to warrant stripping, or if it should simply be scrapped. Assuming that it is worth the cost, compatibility with the selected stripping method must be determined. The type and quantity of coatings also strongly influence the performance of the stripping method. In some instances, simple compatibility may not be sufficient. Engineered components may require specific heat treatments that may be compromised by thermal stripping methods.

Evaluation

The best evaluation method for choosing a stripping system is to work with the various vendors and have actual coated samples processed by them. Their reports should contain basic information such as how much coating was stripped, how long it took, and whether any secondary cleaning operations were necessary. Based on these findings and throughput needs, an estimate for capital and operating costs can be generated and compared.

eleven

Quality Control and Troubleshooting

Quality control in the finishing industry requires attention to more than just the coating. In fact, the majority of problems occur for reasons other than coating faults. To assure quality where the coating may be a factor, statistical process control (SPC) can be a useful tool.

SPC

SPC involves measuring the powder-coating process using statistical methods and improving it to reduce variation at desired process levels. It also can help determine the difference between typical variation inherent in the process and special causes of variation that can be detected and eliminated.

A good initial step is to create a process-flow diagram of the system. Be sure to go out on the shop floor and observe how the process is actually performed. Do not rely totally on how supervisors and process engineers think it is performed.

The key control characteristics at each step of the process are read to derive the flow chart. These key control characteristics are important variables that can be monitored using SPC charts. A typical list of key variables to monitor may include:

- film thickness,
- oven-cure schedule,
- powder volume of virgin and reclaim,
- applicator settings, and
- transfer efficiency.

Since SPC is a data-driven, analytical process, the numbers must be reliable with as little variation as possible. The more variance in a reading, the wider the SPC-control-chart limits are for that variable, and the less sensitive it becomes to changes in the process.

Formal experiments will reveal the capability of the measurement system for the parameter of interest. These include tests such as gage reading and repeatability studies, and short-term machine capability studies. Literature is readily available on how these studies are performed.

A quality assurance/control system using SPC enables the powder-coating user to be proactive in preventing defects. It allows decisions to be based upon data rather than on subjective opinions. By using SPC to monitor and improve critical components in the coating process, the quality of the final product will consistently improve, lowering total cost.

QUALITY VARIATIONS

Close attention to a few critical areas will avoid, or at least minimize, a multitude of quality variations. Careful attention should be given to having a clean, dry, compressed-air supply, clean-sieved reclaim powder, well-grounded parts and equipment, humidity-controlled spray-booth air, and regular inspection and replacement of wear parts. The powder-coating equipment should be installed and operated as recommended by the equipment supplier's manual. Follow the recommendations on the powder coating material data sheets. Have a good preventive maintenance program and stringent housekeeping practices.

Troubleshooting

The following tables provide information on how to avoid specific quality variations and how to correct them if they occur. Tables 11-1 through 11-13 provide troubleshooting guides for powder coating operations.

Table 11-1. Troubleshooting guide for iron phosphatizing process

Problem	Cause	Remedy
Poor coating	pH not in range (see "Poor cleaning")	Adjust pH down with acid, up with caustic
Poor cleaning	Temperatures too low	Raise temperature
	Concentration too low	Increase concentration
	Poor exposure to cleaner	Check racking; check nozzles; check pressure, 15–25 psi (103–172 kPa)
Spotty coating/streaking	Contaminated rinses	Check rinse tanks
	Poor cleaning	See "Poor cleaning"
	Poor exposure	Check racking; check nozzles
Rusting	Coating weight too low	Raise temperatures; lengthen time; increase concentration
	Dry-off too slow	Increase temperature in final rinse
	Drying between stages	Run at lower temperatures; better placement of nozzles; use fog nozzles
Solutions foaming	Temperature too low	Raise temperature
	Pressure too high	Check for plugged nozzles
	Pump picking up air	Check pump packing; check water level
Poor paint adhesion	Coating too heavy	Lower temperature; lower concentration
	Poor cleaning	See "Poor cleaning"
	Contamination	Look for source of silicone near washer
	Bad steel	Check raw material for excessive soil

Table 11-2. Troubleshooting guide for zinc phosphatizing process

Problem	Cause	Remedy
Coating weight too low	Phosphate or accelerator concentration too low Temperature too low Process time not enough	Increase concentration Raise temperature Lengthen time
Coating weight too high	Phosphate or accelerator concentration too high Process time too long	Decrease concentration Shorten time
Powder on coating	Poor rinses Excessive sludge Accelerator concentration too high	Keep rinses overflowing De-sludge tank Allow concentration to drop
Spotty coating	Poor cleaning Low concentration of phosphatizer or accelerator Poor solution coverage Resistant metal	Check cleaning tank Increase concentration Check racking and nozzles Add Jernstedt salts to rinse or cleaner tank
Rusting	Coating weight too low Final dry-off too slow Dry-off between stages	See "Problem—coating weight too low" Increase temperature in the final rinse—use air blow-off Better placement of nozzles; use fog nozzles; run at lower temperatures
Streaking	Poor cleaning Poor rinsing Dry-off between stages	Check cleaning stage Keep rinses overflowing Better arrangement of nozzles; use fog nozzles; run at lower temperatures

Table 11-3. Troubleshooting guide for chromium phosphate process

Problem	Cause	Remedy
Bath pickles metal and creates dusty coating	Accelerator level too high	Reduce accelerator level by processing aluminum or auto draining* and adjusting the bath
Low coating weight	Aluminum concentration too high in bath	Autodrain* and adjust
	Accelerator too low	Add accelerator
	Concentration too low	Add make-up chemical
	Total acid too high in relation to chromium concentration	Autodrain* bath and adjust
No coating	Total absence of accelerator in bath	Add accelerator
Sludge plugging nozzles	Aluminum concentration in bath too high	Autodrain* bath and adjust
	Alkaline salts dragged into bath	Increase overflow rate of rinse following cleaner

* Autodraining is a technique whereby the solution is simultaneously drained and replenished with fresh water and make-up chemical.

Table 11-4. Troubleshooting guide for black-oxide coating process

Problem	Cause	Remedy
Red, rusty coating on mild steel	Temperature too low	Increase heat to cause solution to boil
	Concentration of bath too high for the type of steel	Dilute bath so it boils at a lower temperature
	Iron contamination in bath	Add proprietary chelating agent at a rate of 1–6 lb/100 gal (0.5–2.7 kg/378.5 L)
Red, rusty coating on high-speed or hard steels	Concentration of bath too high for this type of steel	Dilute bath to boil at 255–275° F (124–135° C) and run for 30–45 minutes
Red, rusty coatings on iron castings	Concentration of bath too high for this metal	Dilute to boil at 255–275° F (124–135° C) and run for 45–60 minutes
No coating on high nickel and/or chromium steels	If these steels will coat at all, it will generally be at high temperatures	Increase concentration of bath to boil at 300–320° F (149–160° C)
No coating formed on mild steel	Thin, invisible oxide film on metal surface	Run metal through muriatic pickle
	Iron contamination in bath	Add proprietary chelating agent
	Iron and/or carbon contamination	Add proprietary chelating agent or freeze out carbonate by dropping temperature to under 200° F (93° C)
White, streaky deposits on parts when dried	Excessively contaminated rinse	Dump, rinse, and refill; maintain good overflow

Table 11-5. Troubleshooting guide for fluidized bed operation

Problem	Cause	Remedy
Dusting—powder blowing out of hopper	Air pressure too high	Adjust air regulator to lower pressure to fluid bed
	Powder too fine	Too much reclaim added to virgin powder; virgin powder pulverized too fine by manufacturer
No air—percolating through powder surface	Insufficient air pressure	Check air supply, increase air-regulator pressure; check air-line size to equipment*
	Plugged membrane	Check membrane for plugged pores from dirty air supply
	Obstructed membrane	Check bottom of bed for plastic, cardboard, or other large obstructions
	Compacted powder	Manually loosen powder and fluidize well with clean, dry air

Table 11-5. (continued)

Problem	Cause	Remedy
Rat holing—air blowing large jet holes through powder surface	Powder level too low	Add powder until hopper is 2/3 full when fluidized
	Packed or moist powder	Manually loosen powder and fluidize well with clean, dry air; check compressed air and booth air for high humidity
	Obstructed membrane	Check bottom of bed for plastics, cardboard, or other large obstructions
	Plugged or broken membrane	Check membrane for plugged pores from dirty air supply, cracks, or holes
Stratification—powder separating into layers of fine and coarse particles	Powder level too high	Remove powder until 2/3 full when fluidized
	Powder too fine	Too much reclaim added to virgin powder; virgin powder pulverized too fine by manufacturer

* Follow equipment manual instructions and specifications.

Table 11-6. Troubleshooting guide for hoses and pumps—venturi operation

Problem	Cause	Remedy
Plugged from impact fusion—hard build-up	Normal build-up	Clean or replace parts
	Air pressure too high	Turn down air settings on pumps and guns
	Moisture in air supply	Check air supply for clean, dry air
	Composition of powder feed hoses	Check hoses
	Worn venturis and wear parts	Replace worn parts*
	Powder too fine	Too much reclaim added to virgin powder; virgin powder pulverized too fine by manufacturer
	Powder type or formula	Some resin types tend to have more impact fusion; check with powder supplier
Insufficient powder feed	Powder not fluidizing	See Table 11-5
	Obstruction from contaminated powder supply	Clean out venturis and hoses*
		Check powder supply for contamination; sieve all reclaim before using
	Kinked or flattened hoses	Replace if permanently deformed; avoid sharp bends; use hose saddles for reciprocators; run hoses in covered trench across traffic aisles
	Worn pump venturis	Replace worn parts*
	Low air pressure	Check air supply; adjust all settings to pumps and guns

* Follow equipment manual instructions and specifications.

Table 11-7. Troubleshooting guide for electrostatic coating operation

Problem	Cause	Remedy
Poor charging—inadequate powder build or wrap on part	High-voltage source not providing enough kV at charging electrode or grid	Check high-voltage source is on; systematically check electrical continuity from voltage source to electrode (grid)* including cable, resistors, and fuses; replace missing or broken electrode (grid); clean electrode (grid) insulated by powder build or impact fusion
	Poor ground	Check ground from conveyor rail (or rub bar when used) through hanger to part; all contact areas must be free of powder build, heavy grease, and other insulating material
	Powder delivery (feed) is too high	Turn down powder feed until all material passing through charging corona (field) is adequately charged
	Excessive moisture in powder booth air	Moisture in humid air will tend to dissipate humidity in the powder spray area
	Powder too fine	Too much reclaim added to virgin powder; virgin powder pulverized too fine by manufacturer
	Powder type or formula	Some resin types charge better than others and some formulas are designed for thin film application; check with powder supplier
	Powder delivery air too high Powder blowing by part	Turn down air setting or move gun position farther away from part

Table 11-7. (continued)

Problem	Cause	Remedy
Poor penetration—powder will not coat Faraday cage areas (holes, grooves, channels, inside corners, and recesses)	Powder delivery too low	Turn up powder-delivery air setting; use gun barrel extension
	Poor ground	Check ground
	Powder spray pattern too wide	Select smaller deflector or use suitable slotted barrel and cover (consult equipment supplier)
	Voltage too high	Turn voltage setting down so powder builds on part edges and leading surfaces do not repel powder from corner
	Powder delivery velocity too high	Turn air settings down so powder/air stream does not blow powder out of corners
	Poor gun placement	Adjust gun position so powder cloud has a direct path to recess area
	Powder too fine	Too much reclaim added to virgin powder; virgin powder pulverized too fine by manufacturer
Back-charging—powder layers are repelled from part in spots	Voltage too high	Turn down voltage setting
	Gun positioned too close to part	Change gun placement away from part
	Poor ground	Check ground
	Powder too fine	Too much reclaim added to virgin powder; virgin powder pulverized too fine by manufacturer

143

Table 11-7. (continued)

Problem	Cause	Remedy
Powder picks up a random charge through powder or in fluid path; reverse charging usually through reclaim system	Powder booth air too dry	Adjust powder-spray area humidity (see chart for optimum conditions)
	Poor delivery and/or reclaim usually through equipment ground	Provide ground for all equipment*
Powder feed spurting or slugging—interrupted powder feed	Insufficient air pressure or volume	Check air supply; air-supply piping to equipment is large enough; enough air volume when other equipment such as reverse air cleaning in reclaim housing pulses; air pressure to powder feed does not drop*
	Hoses kinked, flattened, or too long	Check powder feed hoses
	Hoses, pump venturis, or guns clogged with powder	Clean hoses, venturis, and guns*; check air supply for moisture that causes powder compaction; check powder's free-flowing properties; check spray-booth air humidity; check powder supply for contamination; check reclaim sieve
Poor spray pattern—not a symmetrical powder cloud (not applicable when using special deflectors for desired effect)	Worn electrostatic gun parts	Replace worn feed tubes, orifices, deflectors, and covers*
	Impact fusion build	Clean gun parts as needed*
	Delivery (feed) air too low	Check air supply; increase air for powder feed
	Hoses, venturis, or gun blocked with powder	Clean hoses, venturis, and guns*

* Follow equipment manual instructions and specifications.

144

Table 11-8. Troubleshooting guide for collection and reclamation operation

Problem	Cause	Remedy
Contamination in reclaim powder	Reclaim in-line sieve torn, missing, or inoperable	Replace sieve or repair as necessary
	Powder or dirt falling in spray booth from conveyor or hangers	Clean conveyor regularly (or continuously) before entering powder spray booth; strip hangers as needed
	Contamination from parts entering spray booth	Check cleaning and pretreatment equipment and ensure proper part drainage before entering spray booth
	Contamination from plant air circulated through spray booth	Isolate spray-booth area; preferably enclose in a room with filtered, humidity-controlled air
Spray booth dusting—inadequate airflow through spray booth	Bag or cartridge filters binding	Clean or replace bags or cartridge filters*
	Final filters clogged	Check spray booth air humidity
		Check filter bags or cartridges for powder leakage; repair or replace as needed
	Too large of open area in spray booth housing	Reduce open area; increased opening reduces booth's air velocity*
	Powder delivery (feed) too high	Reduce the number of spraying guns or the amount of powder to each gun*

* Follow equipment manual instructions and specifications.

Table 11-9. Troubleshooting guide for finish-cured-film physical properties

Problem	Cause	Remedy
Poor impact resistance/ poor flexibility	Undercured	Increase oven temperature or increase dwell time in oven
	Poor cleaning or pretreatment	Check pretreatment equipment and chemicals
	Film thickness too high	Reduce film thickness by adjusting application equipment*
	Change in substrate thickness or type	Check substrate with supplier
	Powder resin type or formula	Check with powder manufacturer
Poor adhesion	Poor cleaning or pretreatment	Check pretreatment equipment and chemicals*
	Change in substrate	Check substrate with supplier
	Undercured	Increase oven temperature or increase dwell time in oven
	Powder resin type or formula	Check with powder manufacturer
Poor corrosion resistance	Poor cleaning or pretreatment	Check pretreatment equipment and chemicals*
	Undercured	Increase oven temperature or increase dwell time in oven
Poor chemical resistance	Undercured	Increase oven temperature or increase dwell time in oven
	Powder resin type or formula	Check with powder manufacturer
Poor pencil hardness/poor abrasion resistance	Undercured	Increase oven dwell time
	Powder-resin type or formula	Check with powder manufacturer

* Follow equipment manual instructions and specifications.

Table 11-10. Troubleshooting guide for coating finish-cured-film appearance

Problem	Cause	Remedy
Poor surface flow—too much orange peel	Film thickness too thin	Increase film thickness by adjusting application equipment
	Heat-up rate too slow	Increase oven temperature or modify oven baffling to increase heat rate
	Powder-resin type or formula	Check with powder manufacturer
Gloss too low for high-gloss powder	Incompatible powder contamination	Clean application equipment before changing powders
	Micro-pinholing from gassing	Check substrate for porosity; check substrate for moisture; check powder for moisture from reclaim or compressed air; check film thickness, coating too thick
	Powder-resin type or formula	Check with powder manufacturer
Gloss too high for a low-gloss-type powder	Undercured	Increase temperature of oven or increase dwell time in oven
	Powder formula	Check with powder manufacturer
Contamination in powder	See Table 11-8; virgin powder contaminated	Check with powder manufacturer

Table 11-10. (continued)

Problem	Cause	Remedy
Inconsistent film thickness	Guns positioned wrong	Check and reposition guns so spray patterns overlap slightly
	Reciprocators not matched to line speed	Adjust line speed or adjust reciprocator stroke*
	Airflow in booth disturbing spray pattern	Consult equipment supplier
	Defective spray equipment	Go through application checklist
Off color	Improper oven exhaust	Check exhaust vent fan(s)*
	Bake time too long	Adjust line speed
	Oven temperature too high	Lower oven temperature
	Variation in film thickness	See "Inconsistent film thickness"
	Powder formulated	Check with powder manufacturer
Pinholing and gassing through coating surface		See "Gloss too low for high-gloss powder"
Pull-away or tearing— coating film shrinks leaving bare substrate	Uncharged powder	See application section, poor charging
	Poor cleaning, metal preparation, or dryoff	Check pretreatment equipment, dryoff oven, and part drainage

* Follow equipment manual instructions and specifications.

Table 11-11. Output of powder insufficient to coat parts

Problem	Cause	Remedy
Poor fluidizing properties in the powder hopper	Pressure of fluidizing air too low	Adjust (increase) pressure of fluidizing air
	Fluidizing membrane is blocked	Clean or replace the fluidizing membrane: see instructions of equipment supplier
	Humidity of compressed air too high	Install an air dryer with a corresponding oil-micro filter or another suitable drying system
	Humidity of the powder too high	Check storage facilities; powder should be stocked at room temperature in closed packing (maximum humidity 75%)
	Free-flowing properties of the powder are bad	Contact powder supplier
Blockage in venturis and hoses	Fusing of the powder in the venturi	Clean or replace the venturi (see instructions of the equipment supplier); if necessary, reduce pressure of powder or transport air
	Fusing of the powder in the hoses	Clean the hose by bending and breaking up the fused powder; if necessary, replace it; install an air dryer with a corresponding oil micro-filter or another suitable drying system
	Bad free-flowing properties of the powder	Contact powder supplier

Table 11-11. (continued)

Problem	Cause	Remedy
Blockage in the gun	Fusing in the gun or gun outlet	Clean the gun according to the instructions of the equipment supplier; when blocking occurs, frequently check humidity of compressed air and the free-flowing properties of the powder
	Blockage caused by contamination of the powder with dust of other coarse materials	Clean the gun according to the instructions of the equipment supplier and determine the reason for the contamination (check powder pumps for possible impact fusion; impact fusion particles that break off in the pump could be transported to the spray gun and result in blockage)

Table 11-12. Poor or insufficient coverage

Problem	Cause	Remedy
Insufficient wrap-around	Poor electrostatic charging of the powder; output of powder too low	Adjust level of electrostatic kV (increase); if not possible, check equipment and guns according to instructions of equipment supplier; check for broken electrodes on the spray gun, if found, replace electrodes; check for possible frictional transport through powder hose, if evident, consult powder supplier for hose material recommendation
	Insufficient ground contact	Check the ground contacts using a suitable resistance measuring device; correct and ensure sufficient earth-to-ground control
	Using an unsuitable powder type	Contact powder supplier
Poor penetration into corners, flanges, slots, etc.	Output of powder too low	See "Insufficient wrap-around"
	Insufficient ground contact	Check the ground contacts and if necessary use a suitable measuring instrument
	Powder cloud too wide	Narrow powder cloud; if necessary, install a more suitable deflector or adjust air for cone

Table 11-12. (continued)

Problem	Cause	Remedy
Poor adherence of powder to part, powder falls from part easily	Poor electrostatic charging of powder	Adjust level of electrostatic kV (increase); if not possible, check equipment and guns according to instructions of equipment supplier; see "Insufficient wrap-around"
	Powder output too high or the pressure for the transport air is too high, which blows the powder from the object	Reduce powder output and/or reduce pressure of the transport air
	Unsuitable particle-size distribution of the powder or unsuitable powder type for the objects	Contact powder supplier

Table 11-13. Disturbance in cured film

Problem	Cause	Remedy
Dust, precured or other coarse material	Dust or other coarse parts on the metal surface	Check pretreatment
	Dust or other coarse parts in powder; precured material from original powder which is stocked according to the instructions	Check powder and locate the cause of the contamination; if necessary, clean up the installation and use fresh or sieved powder
Matting of powder surface	Contamination with other powder (based on other raw materials)	Clean up the installation; if necessary, contact powder supplier
Orange peel	Warm-up of the coated material is too slow or too fast	Check curing cycle and curing oven; if necessary, contact powder supplier
	Powder type; too fast or too coarse particle-size distribution	Contact powder supplier
	Moisture contamination	Replace the powder
	Heat damage of the powder	Replace the powder
Cratering	Contamination with other powder (based on other raw materials)	Clean up the installation; if necessary, contact powder supplier
	Bad pretreatment with, for example, remaining greases	Check pretreatment and, if necessary, contact pretreatment supplier
	Contamination with incompatible materials from the spraying area, such as silicones	Check for the presence of incompatible materials if necessary, clean up the installation and contact powder supplier

Table 11-13. (continued)

Problem	Cause	Remedy
Pinholing	Humidity of the powder too high	Check storage facilities; powder should be stocked at room temperature in closed packing (maximum humidity 75%)
	Air entrapment with casting	Preheat objects over 320° F (160° C) and cool down before application (only galvanized), or contact powder supplier who can recommend a special powder
	Gas entrapment and escapement due to chemical reaction	Keep coating thickness below 0.004 in. (100 μm); if necessary, contact powder supplier

appendix I

The Future of Powder Coating

By Greg Bocchi, Executive Director
The Powder Coating Institute

Powder coating remains the fastest growing industrial finishing method in North America, currently representing about 15% of the total industrial finishing market. There are about 5,000 powder coating operations in North America applying powder to a countless array of products for automobiles; appliances; furniture for the office, home, and outdoors; lawn and garden products; store fixtures and shelving; sporting goods equipment; aluminum extrusions and other building components; and more. Powder coating provides a durable, high-quality finish that resists scratches, corrosion, abrasion, chemicals, and detergents.

ADVANTAGES

Environmental advantages have led the way for powder coating conversion in North America, as powder coating offers maximum compliance with increasingly stringent environmental regulations. Because powder coating contains no solvents, the process emits negligible, if any, polluting volatile organic compounds into the atmosphere, and does not require venting, filtering, and solvent recovery systems as are necessary with liquid finishing processes. Exhaust air from the coating booth can be safely returned to the coating room, and less oven air is exhausted to the outside, making the powder-coating process a safer and cleaner finishing alternative. It also saves considerable energy.

Since it is a dry process, most powder-coating overspray, up to 98%, can be readily retrieved and reused. The unused powder is reclaimed by a recovery unit and returned to a feed hopper for recirculating through the system. The waste that results is negligible, and can be disposed of easily and economically.

Greater efficiency is achieved because powder coating requires no drying or flash-off time, parts can be racked closer together on a conveyor, and more parts can be coated automatically. Powder-coating material does not run, drip, or sag. This results in significantly lower reject rates.

While these environmental and operational advantages translate to economical advantages, there are additional cost savings associated with powder coating. Minimum operator training and supervision are required for a powder line. Employees prefer working with dry powder over liquid paints because of its lack of fumes, reduced housekeeping problems, and minimum contamination of clothing. Also, compliance with federal and state regulations is easier, which saves both time and money.

MATERIALS

In recent years, research and development in powder coating materials has resulted in new formulations. Specific appearance characteristics in powder-coating materials include:

- Color and gloss variety is almost limitless, with the availability of off-the-shelf colors and custom color-match services, as well as clear coats.
- Flat and high glosses are available. Matte finishes, which can hide surface imperfections, as well as hammertones and veins, provide stylish antique and weathered looks, along with fluorescent and pearl-like finishes.
- Photoluminescent powder coatings, which absorb ultraviolet, fluorescent, or incandescent light to gradually re-emit the light, are used for road signs, hazard warnings, and markings on trucks, buses, and police cars.
- Metallic coatings add sparkling highlights to reproduce the appearance of the base metal and add richness to the look of the product.

- Textured and wrinkle finishes can hide substrate irregularities, provide a nonslipping surface, hide fingerprints, offer excellent resistance to high wear and weatherability, and give the product a distinctive feel. Appearances can vary from the look of fine sandpaper, to a pebbly texture, to a rougher look resembling alligator skin.

Powder materials today have a wider variety of performance characteristics, which have increased their versatility in a wide variety of applications. Specially formulated powders offer increased resistance to weathering for outdoor applications such as stadium seating. Electro-conductive and electro-dissipative powders protect electronic components. Hygienic and antibacterial powders are used on products for kitchens, restaurants, and hospitals. Powders resistant to high heat are used for charcoal grills and engine exhaust components. Thin-film powders of 0.8–1.2 mils (20–31 μm) thick are available, and there are powders that can cure at lower temperatures for heat-sensitive substrates such as plastics and wood. Some powders for use on heat-sensitive substrates and components are formulated to cure by ultraviolet radiation in a matter of seconds.

APPLICATIONS

Concurrent with the advancements in powder formulation are new and innovative ways to apply the powder. An overview of these advancements follows:

- Color change time has been reduced significantly with the availability of new powder booths to repel the powder, automated belt and sweepers to direct overspray powder to recovery systems, and streamlined powder delivery systems.
- Coil coating with powder can produce deep textures in a single pass, along with unique visual effects not possible with liquid processes.
- Blank coating of pre-cut metal sheets, which are then post-formed prior to final assembly, remains a strong growth area, particularly in the appliance market.

- In-mold coating is a process that sprays powder onto a heated mold cavity before the molding cycle begins, and the powder chemically bonds to the molding compound for a finish that is chip and impact resistant.
- Radiation curing, either through infrared, ultraviolet, or electron beam, has opened up new applications for the powder coating of heat-sensitive substrates such as wood, wood-based materials, plastic parts, and assembled components, reducing the curing temperature to below 250° F (121° C). Curing can be accomplished in a matter of seconds. One of the most successful new radiation curing applications is medium-density fiberboard (MDF) made of wood particles with a synthetic resin. MDF is used for ready-to-assemble furniture for the home and office, bathroom and kitchen cabinets, store fixtures and displays, and barbecue trays and shelves.

New applications for powder coating are increasing all the time, leading to uses that were unfathomable just a few years ago. Ongoing technological advancements in materials, equipment, application methods, and curing ensure that powder coatings will occupy an ever-increasing share of the finishing market.

appendix II

Sales Growth and Diversification

Adapted from "Sales Growth and Diversification for Finishing Shops through Vertical Integration of Processes" by Michael Feldstein

Retention of customers, growth of sales, and developing new customers are goals shared by virtually all finishing job shops. Aside from the traditional methods of sales and marketing, diversification is often a course chosen to meet these goals. Most commonly, however, shops contemplate only the incorporation of similar or competing processes as a method of diversification.

HORIZONTAL INTEGRATION

Examples of diversification include a plating shop adding anodizing capabilities, or a painting company acquiring a powder-coating line. Such additions may be different from the processes previously performed, but generally only represent a small degree of horizontal integration. Such integration may be a natural and appropriate route to growth if properly pursued. Similar processes can complement a shop's existing production, administration, and marketing capabilities. The current staff is likely to be capable of implementing the new process without much training or expense. There may, however, be significant limitations to the adoption of a horizontal technology. Care must be taken not to horizontally add a new process that will shift business away from an existing process (unless of course, the shop is in danger of losing business in the existing process to another provider of the same technology). Too often, new technologies are adopted without sufficient consideration. Shop owners hear stories of success in new and different fields and may be led to believe that the grass is greener in another segment of the industry.

VERTICAL INTEGRATION

Vertical integration is achieved when a company acquires companies or technologies involved in different levels of the same supply chain to satisfy a broader range of customer requirements. Here's how it works.

First, find out exactly what happens to a customer's parts before and after they are processed in your job shop. Are there other finishing-related operations being performed on the parts by another vendor or customer?

Next, determine if the customer would be interested in having your shop perform these other operations as well. If so, calculate the cost of developing the other process, the price for which you can perform the other technology, and the benefits that this vertical integration will provide to you and your customer. Benefits to the customer include pricing, logistical, administrative, and quality factors such as:

- Costs of processing and shipping are naturally lower when subsequent processes are consolidated into one facility.
- Turnaround time is inherently less when processes are vertically integrated.
- One-stop shopping provides substantial logistical efficiencies including shipping coordination and packaging.
- Reducing the number of vendors also reduces administrative requirements in accounting and quality systems management.
- Concentration of the responsibility for quality to one vendor means no finger pointing between vendors, and less repetitive handling and chance of damage or loss of parts.

The theory of vertical integration for finishing shops is not just getting more work in the door, but doing more work on what is already coming in.

The benefits to a job shop include:

- providing greater value to customers, leading to business retention and referrals;
- more efficient production scheduling of subsequent processes;
- better control of quality;
- opportunities to attract new customers through new technologies; and
- the potential to extend to customers of new technologies the also use of traditional processes.

Case Study

Here is a case study that is a great example of how this theory and strategy can be implemented to the benefit of a finishing job shop and its customers, old and new.

Surface Technology, Inc. (STI), founded in 1973 and located in Trenton, New Jersey, is a high-end plating shop specializing in composite electroless nickel (EN) plating. The company's services include composite EN plating with materials ranging from diamond or silicon carbide for wear resistance to boron nitride or Teflon® for lubricity; as well as a full line of conventional EN baths. All plating is accomplished with STI's own line of proprietary EN solutions for optimal control of quality and economy.

STI does plating for customers in numerous industries around the world. The company has always had a unique approach to commercializing its extensive knowledge in the plating field via solution sales, service, licensing, consulting, and contract research and development.

In recent years, STI has pursued a strategy of diversification by vertical integration according to the requirements of its customers. This strategy has provided significant value to many of its customers and growth for STI.

To retain customers and increase revenue, STI thoroughly investigates the broader uses and requirements of its customers' parts. As STI's coatings generally are functional and not decorative in nature, STI first ascertains the applications in which they are used. From there, STI works closely with its customers to learn about the processes performed on the parts before and/or after they are coated by STI.

In one application, for example, STI established that before certain high-wear steel parts were sent to STI for its patented composite diamond coating, the steel was being hardened by a diffusion process. STI subsequently invested time and resources to develop its Bor-Fuse® hardening process. This process diffuses hard boron material below the surface of steel parts to achieve a hardness of 2,000 Vickers (about 84–86 HRC) to a depth of up to 0.005 in. (0.13 mm). Subsequent to the Bor-Fuse process, parts can be coated in the same facility. The implementation of this hardening process has allowed a number of STI's customers to eliminate one vendor in the product manufacturing sequence, thereby reducing the total processing time even more. Quality of the parts is also enhanced because STI is able to insure the work of one process is accomplished with consideration for the surface requirements of the subsequent process.

In another example, STI determined that certain high-precision parts were being deburred and polished prior to delivery for coating at STI. STI used its expertise in electroless chemical processes to develop Deburr 1000®, a chemical deburring and polishing system for steel. The cleaning process required for parts prior to Deburr 1000 was essentially the same as for conventional EN pretreatment. To add Deburr 1000 to STI's primary plating line, therefore, required the addition of only one tank for the Deburr 1000 chemistry itself, and one dedicated rinse tank. Parts that previously had to be sent to two vendors for two distinct processes (involving two round-trip shipments, twice handling delicate parts with packing and unpacking, two invoices, etc.) are now processed in one combined cycle at STI's facility. The time and cost savings to customers are substantial.

STI has also found ways to integrate new post-plating processes to satisfy customer requirements. When a customer's molds, coated with NiSlip® 500 composite electroless nickel with Teflon, needed additional release properties, STI developed a process to diffuse even more Teflon into the coating after plating. This process is now available as NiSlip 500+.

Similarly, when STI learned of a customer's routine of sending parts with STI's NiPlate® 700 (a composite EN with fine silicon-carbide particles) for subsequent polishing at another facility, STI looked into doing it in house. Through research coordinated with the customer, STI developed the know-how for a mass finishing technique to meet the customer's requirements. In this instance, having the parts handled by two companies led to finger pointing between the coater and the subsequent polishing vendor when damage or irregularities arose. STI realized that it would be better to take full responsibility for the quality and integrity of the parts, while saving the customer time, money, and administration effort.

Each of these examples demonstrates benefits to the customer provided by vertical integration at the finishing job shop. The benefits to the shop are also significant. First and foremost, STI has retained and increased business with existing customers. Its customers view STI as an innovative partner with shared interests in mind. STI has also marketed its new technologies to a new array of customers in two general ways.

First, STI sells Bor-Fuse and Deburr 1000 products to a wide variety of finishing shops. The adoption of either the Bor-Fuse or Deburr 1000 process by another finishing shop is facilitated by STI's ability to do initial trials of their parts at STI's facility, and then transfer the know-how so the process can be performed by the finishing shop. STI has also introduced these new technologies to existing customers of EN plating services worldwide. These longstanding buyers are enthusiastic to adopt additional processes that can allow them to also offer a broader array of vertically integrated services to their own customers. They are particularly confident in adopting processes from STI because they recognize that they are the same processes used by STI itself. This assures them of the greatest performance, reliability, and economy.

Second, after new customers purchase newer technologies, like Bor-Fuse and Deburr 1000, STI is also able to offer them its traditional coating services. In this manner, STI has demonstrated that vertical integration can be a two-way street (Feldstein 2001).

REFERENCE

Feldstein, Michael. 2001. "Sales Growth and Diversification for Finishing Shops Through Vertical Integration of Processes." Technical Paper FC01-350. Dearborn MI: Society of Manufacturing Engineers.

appendix III

Juggling Customers, Competitors, Compliance, and Change

Adapted from "21st Century Shops: Juggling Customers, Competitors, Compliance, and Change"
by Greg Yahn

The worlds of business and manufacturing are going through phenomenal changes. Global markets, virtual technology, and wireless transfer of information will shape the future of every existing industry, as well as create many new ones. As the manufacturers of metal, plastic, and wood products constantly improve production methods to reduce the cost of products, powder coating as a finish will become more important, and of course, more competitive. How will the most basic provider of powder coating, the job shop, survive?

No matter how much time is lost by design and engineering delays, material supplier delays, and production delays, when the parts arrive at the door for powder coating, the customer needs them yesterday! This is the reality of the job-shop powder coater. Finishers are not wizards possessing magical powers, yet, the title *finisher* suggests that the many delays that a customer incurs through the manufacturing process can somehow be overcome, and the delivery promise met.

EVOLUTION OF THE JOB SHOP

Just as the giant Boeing 747 had its roots at Kitty Hawk, and the aircraft carrier USS Enterprise ultimately sprang from a dugout canoe, most of the largest powder-coating companies started small and grew larger with time. As with all evolutionary processes, Darwinian theory seems to sort out the survivors and the failures. The survivors tend to fall into four categories: Mom-and-pop (garage) shops, small coaters, large coaters, and original equipment manufacturer (OEM) coaters.

Mom-and-Pop and Garage Shops

Most powder-coating companies started out as small mom-and-pop shops or garage shops. Used equipment of all sizes and capacities is available on the second-hand market (as leftovers from failures or trade-ins from survivors). Used equipment is much less expensive than new equipment. Although a used oven may not have state-of-the-art controls or bells and whistles, it keeps the overhead down.

Far more important than the equipment is the proprietor's ability to manage a business and move up the learning curve. Mistakes can be costly, and the key to survival is building a knowledge base and reputation for quality. As a business grows, it will only be successful if its leaders learn how to keep costs low and profits high, and make capital investments wisely. Used-equipment dealers have warehouses full of shiny new pieces of equipment that put mom and pop out of business when they bought all that new equipment and then could not make the payments on it.

Small Coaters

If mom and pop are successful, they may grow their business into a small powder-coating company. The majority of powder-coating companies in America are considered small. They are job shops that may have anywhere from 5–50 employees and sales of up to $10 million. Most small coaters have 20–200 customers, and 80% of them are within a 100-mile radius. Capacities may vary, but most have both line and batch capabilities. They may use vapor degreasing or automatic wash lines, and manual or automatic spray guns. Equipment is usually a mix of new and used, but if they are successful, they know how to use it, and how to get more out of it than the manufacturer intended.

As with most small businesses, the key to survival is good management, hard work, and satisfied customers. Probably the single most difficult decision for the small coater is when and how much to grow. It is also important to note that an increase in size usually means a required improvement in structure. As small businesses grow, the need for better communication and training, and a more defined business structure becomes more imperative. When that big job comes along, the company that bids low, buys more capacity, and scrambles to stay on top of the job, may very well be the next deal for the salvage company. However, the company that does its homework, prepares for the growth, and makes that job profitable is one step closer to evolving to the next level, the large coater.

Large Coaters

Large powder-coating companies are truly amazing businesses. The sheer volume of product finished in one hour can stagger the imagination. Hundreds of employees hang thousands of parts each hour for a variety of customers. Fixtures and equipment allow high levels of efficiency. Statistical process control (SPC) and quality control keep rejects in the parts per million, and material usage at a minimum. A large coater may use 10,000 lb (4,536 kg) of one powder on one job in a month and have less than 100 lb (45 kg) outstanding.

Though large coaters may have started in a garage, their management has made the right decisions as to when to grow, how to price jobs, how to utilize resources effectively, and how to manage their evolution with control and structure. That is not to say that they have not made mistakes, but they have learned from those mistakes and taken corrective action to avoid them in the future. This is key to the evolution of the powder-coating job shop.

OEM Coaters

Although an OEM coater has the benefit of having a captive customer, many OEM coaters have excess capacity and compete in the realm of the powder-coating job shop. Though they have the advantage of a guaranteed workload, they face the same pitfalls as the small coater. As the OEM coater competes in the open market, the challenges of capacity, scheduling, flexibility, and growth, affect them as well. In fact, some successful OEM coaters, at the benefit of their parent company, branch out to become independent finishers, and ultimately large powder coaters.

HOW MOST JOB SHOPS OPERATE

Most powder-coating job shops operate in a similar fashion, regardless of size. Whether large or small, the name of the game is profit. The question is, "What kind of jobs can be run to best fit capacity and generate the most profit?" Obviously, the market will determine what jobs are available, and the hard question is, "What jobs should be let go?" There are four basic types of jobs that a job shop has to choose from. The first three are roots of the fourth. They are the one-time job, the occasional job, the repeat job, and the "carrot" job. Each type has its advantages and disadvantages.

One-time Jobs

One-time jobs are just that, one time. Whether it is Joe's bumper or the Liberty Bell, chances are it will only be powder coated once. There are actually more one-time jobs than any other type of job in the market. Because of the nature of powder coating, when done correctly, a product will only need to be finished once, and that finish will exceed the life of the product. Chances are, Joe will probably sell his truck before the bumper needs to be recoated. The advantage of this type of job is that it is usually a good fill-in if the customer has no time constraint. If it is a rush job, a premium can be charged. The downside is the material cost. If the customer wants a specific color or material, the cost of the material alone can make the job uneconomical.

Occasional Jobs

Occasional jobs are usually same-lot production runs. They are seasonal products that are in demand only in limited quantities, but are required the same time each year, such as snow shovels, rakes, and electric-heater housings. Volume may increase if the product is successful, and the job may never come back if it is not. Or, the job may be parts run for stock inventory but not quick sellers. An economically viable order quantity is run to maintain a competitive price, and the job does not return until the inventory is depleted. The advantage of occasional jobs lies in the fact that with each production run, the efficiency gets better, but the price remains the same or increases. The downside is the same as with a one-time job. If powder is purchased for the job based on the initial quantity, the price is higher and either the profit or the potential of getting the job is lower.

Repeat Jobs

Repeat jobs, especially those under contract, are the powder coating job shops job of choice. Whether daily, weekly, monthly, or quarterly, the repeat job offers the greatest potential for profit. When quoting a potential repeat job, the coater has several options to offer the customer. A flat piece price, a quantity discount price, a price ramp down to share the benefits of the learning curve, elimination of a set up charge, a one-time tooling and fixturing charge, and volume discount on material costs, are all options available to a job shop when quoting a repeat job. The main advantages are the security of the repeat business and the opportunity to improve the efficiency of the job, and therefore the improvement of profit margin. The downside is the cost of misquoting the job. If a contract is signed and it is found out after the second production run that something was missed, the job can quickly go from a potential winner to a definite loser.

Carrot Jobs

Carrot jobs come in all shapes and sizes. A carrot job is usually the end product of an extremely optimistic entrepreneur who is convinced that this job is the better mousetrap. "If it can be finished at a lower cost, it will be initially competitive. This will allow it to gain market share and take off to become the best thing since the pet rock. After the initial low piece run, the volumes will grow to millions within months!" Nine times out of ten, this is the scenario, and the job is never seen again. However, a successful entrepreneur has the memory of an elephant, and if and when that product is successful, if you helped out, you have the contract. If not, your competitor will thank you.

Another type of carrot job is the hybrid. It is the one-timer that may become an occasional, or the occasional that may become a repeat. The advantages and disadvantages are proportional to the level of investment, research, and intuition applied. Many carrot jobs, over time, turn out to be well worth the effort. The beauty of the successful ones lies in the fact that the finisher is often largely responsible for their success.

COMPETITION

If you own or work for a powder coating job shop, chances are there is a competitor within 60 miles of you. You may not even know they exist, and they may not know about you either. In some cases, competition may be relatively friendly, and shops may even share jobs and powder. In other cases, competition may be brutal, and competing shops may consistently underbid jobs to keep customers. Either way, there are several general types of jobs, and each firm will have their own way of selling to the customer.

Local Jobs

Most jobs a powder-coating shop does are local. Even if the shop has its own truck, freight costs often make out-of-town jobs difficult to compete on. Depending on the size of the city and the business environment there, foundries, fabricators, and stamping houses are usually the main source of work. If a large industry, such as the automotive industry, has a plant in the city, several powder coaters may service that one company. Usually a small powder-coating shop will need at least several local jobs to keep busy. Larger shops may need several dozen. Depending on the state of competition between firms, some customers may take advantage of the market environment and continually request requotes and price reductions. This often leads to the elimination of one firm, as the profit margins become too small for them to survive. For most companies, local jobs are the bread and butter of the business.

Niche Jobs

Because firms are built and grown by different people and on different jobs, each company's capacity will differ. Rarely are all competitors in a market armed with the same tools and equipment. Also, because different companies will purchase capital to run different jobs, they inherently create niches for themselves. A niche job is one that is relatively specialized. Whether it is long parts, assembly, or two-coat or two-color applications, these companies develop an expertise to run certain jobs that differentiate them from their competitors. In many cases, niche jobs are higher margin jobs than most others, mainly because no one else can do them.

Big Opportunities

Once in awhile, a really big job comes along that all of the competitors want. It may be a multi-year contract or high-volume job that will fill the shop's capacity and cover most of the overhead. The firm that lands the job will have both an advantage over its competitors and a hurdle for future opportunities. On one hand, the job will consume much of the company's capacity and assure that the company will remain busy. On the other, the job may cause other customer's product quality and/or deliveries to fall. Also, if the big job requires a smaller profit margin to assure commitment from the customer, other more profitable jobs may be sacrificed.

One other danger that is often present with big opportunities is the tendency of the company to want the job too badly. If proper care is not taken to make sure the job is quoted within the means of the company's resources, or if mistakes are made and details missed, the job can quickly turn into an anchor that ultimately drags the company down. If the job requires the finishing of thousands of parts per week, and the price is low by a dime per piece, and there is a contract involving liquidated damages, the end result is obvious if the company fails to meet expectations.

OEMs

Sometimes a powder-coating job shop will find itself competing with an OEM. This competition may be for an in-house job that the manufacturer wants to outsource, or a local job that the OEM quotes to fill unused capacity. Both scenarios can be very frustrating for the job shop.

Competing with an In-house Line

When a large company with an in-house paint line wants to convert some or all of their painting to powder coating, the local powder-coating companies are usually put on the spot. The OEM has an estimate of its internal finishing costs, and would like the powder coater to do the work at a savings to them. Usually the biggest challenge for the powder coater is to educate the customer about the differences between paint and powder, and obtain an accurate cost of the current painting process. When a union company's cost to paint is $0.02/lb ($0.04/kg), and my non-union shop labor cost is twice their estimate, I know I have an uphill battle. The key to quoting OEM work is to maintain focus on profit goals, and make sure costs and methods have been thoroughly evaluated. If the job does not look like it will make money, it probably will not, and the OEM is better off painting it. However, if the OEM can be educated on the differences in cost and quality of the finished product, you can most likely build a strong and mutually beneficial relationship.

Competing with Extra Capacity

One of the most difficult hurdles a job-shop powder coater can face is competition with an OEM's extra capacity. When a fabricator has an in-house powder-coating line, and they have excess capacity, they often go out into the market to compete on local jobs. Their main advantage is that they can be highly competitive because most of their overhead is absorbed by in-house work. This allows them to be selective in the jobs they want, and effective at taking them away. Usually it is best to compete on delivery and service rather than on price alone, as their in-house product will usually take delivery priority over an outside customer's product.

Remaining Competitive

The challenge to every type of business in the global economy is twofold. It is not good enough to just be competitive; companies also must be profitable. For many powder-coating job shops, the shareholders are the proprietors, the ones in the spray booth, unloading the trucks, or even hanging the parts on the line. Just being competitive is not good enough for them, they want to profit. However, if the competition is strong, they may settle for less profit. And therein lies the challenge. How do you keep focused on the jobs in front of you while still keeping an eye on competition?

Know Your Business

The number one factor for success in the world of finishing is to know your business. Everyone in your organization that is involved in management, sales, production, and quality control should be well versed in the basics of powder coating. What is the difference between a thermoset and a thermoplastic resin? Between line and batch work? Electrostatic spray versus fluid bed dip? Corona versus tribo? Iron phosphate versus zinc phosphate? If your quality control department or sales representative can not answer these questions, chances are, your customers will find someone who can. However, if all key people are well trained and have a full understanding of what your business does, your customers will respect them and seek your advice as well as your business.

Stay Flexible

Flexibility is inherent to a job shop. However, the vision that goes along with that flexibility is often overlooked. If a customer calls about a job that requires a polyvinyl chloride (PVC) coating, and your company currently does not offer it, you may send them on their way to find a copany that does. If a job requires assembly or final packaging, and you are not set up for it, turning that job away has an opportunity cost that may prevent you from doing a substantial amount of work for them in the future. The point is, keeping an open mind to the possibilities is what creates opportunities for the future. One job that is set up for today may lead to another very profitable job tomorrow. The company that limits its vision limits opportunities. The other side of the coin is to learn, research, understand, and control the areas of expansion so as not to dedicate too many resources to a project that has no chance of recovering its cost.

Develop Niche Markets

Niche markets are markets with few or no competitors. They usually involve jobs that are unique or require specialized materials and equipment. The benefit of such jobs is the high profit margin that can be obtained. Most finishers can powder coat doorknobs for Ford at $0.03 each, but how many can coat a cement mixer? The margin on a $0.05 die spring may seem good if you coat 500,000 of them, but can you coat and assemble automatic teller machines? Do you sandblast? Can you coat with Teflon®, nylon, or Kynar®? These are some of the potential niche markets that require time and money to cultivate, but the end result is a profitable supplement to the monthly bottom line.

Quality, Delivery, and Total Customer Satisfaction

Regardless of the type of finishing performed, the path to a profitable business is the same—the customer pays the bills, and if the customer is satisfied, the bills get paid. The best way to keep customers satisfied is to fulfill their basic needs by providing on-time delivery and the quality of finished product expected. A customer who receives quality product on time will be totally satisfied, even if the price is a little higher than the competition.

There is an old saying, "there is never time to do it right, but there is always time to do it over." Rework costs both the company and the customer. If a problem arises and a delivery promise cannot be met, keeping the customer informed of the problem will go a long way to maintaining the relationship, as some mistakes are inevitable. The rule should be "get it done right, and get it done on time." Customers will not only thank you, they will pay you.

SURVIVING IN THE NEW MILLENNIUM
Customers

"The customer is king," "the customer pays the bills," and "the customer is always right," are catch phrases that have stood the test of time. However, in fact, the customer is often ignorant, unreasonable, and may not pay bills on time—all realities of business in the 21st century. The key to a successful relationship with customers is communication.

First, the customer must be educated. It is critical that the customer has no doubt what service is being provided when a job is quoted. From the inbound freight to the packaging and delivery of the finished product, every aspect of the finishing process is the responsibility of the finisher to define. In most cases, the customer has no clue as to how the finished product should be packaged to prevent damage in shipment, so that should be clearly explained in the quote.

Second, the customer must understand the limitations of the finisher. If a company quotes on production quantities of 1,000 pieces and the customer ships 10 pieces this morning and needs them this afternoon, (A) they may not be able to get them, and (B) they will not be at the quoted price. As mentioned earlier, the finisher is not a wizard who is able to magically and instantly finish parts. Ovens must be turned on, fluid beds filled, masking may be required, and all of this takes time and costs money. Certainly a few favors can be done for a good customer, but a good customer does not go to the well too often.

Finally, if a company is to be successful, customers must pay on its terms. It is imperative to do the research on new customers, especially if those customers are large. For the small coater with a large customer, that big job can push account receivables up to $100,000 in one month. If vendor payment terms are 30 days, and payroll is weekly, when the big customer's check comes in 90 days it may come to an empty office. For smaller accounts, although it is very hard to do, holding shipment on an order is better than shipping it for free. That is the disadvantage of being the last link in the production chain. Everyone else had to be paid for the product to reach your door, and there may not be enough left to cover your price. Make sure the customer knows that payment is expected, and that cash-on-delivery (COD) is an acceptable form of payment.

Competitors

Competition is not a bad thing. No matter how small the pond, or how large the business, competition will force improvement. In general, the free-enterprise system forces companies to keep on top of their game. This benefits both the customers and the suppliers. The key is to understand the competition without becoming obsessed with them. What they do should not dictate what you do, for if it does, you are going in the wrong direction. In most markets, competitors vie for some jobs, but individual companies maintain most jobs without competitive threat. This is due to the customer relations that the finishers build with their customer base.

If a new player enters the market and undercuts the existing finishers' prices to gain market share, some customers will inevitably shift to them to gain competitive advantage over their competition. Depending on the abilities of the new company, it may be successful in attracting customers away from the existing finishers. If so, all finishers may have to re-evaluate their profit goals and pricing structures to compensate. (This is where a good niche market comes in handy.) In most cases, this is a positive change. However, if the number of competitors exceeds the volume of work in the market, the competition can increase until one or more of the finishers is forced out of the market.

Compliance

Compliance refers to government regulations. In today's market, compliance can make or break a company. One of the reasons for the success of the powder-coating industry as a whole is the enforcement of government regulations on the liquid paint industry. Before the current state and federal regulation of volatile organic compound emissions, and disposal and handling of paint and solvents, powder coating was, in most applications, not competitive with paint. The need for ovens to cure the powders gave the air-dry painters a cost advantage that kept powder at the edge of the market. Many paint shops even used spent solvents as weed killer around their plants until regulations required reporting on use and manifests of disposal. Today, most government regulations are still mostly focused on the liquid finishing industry. However, as environmental concerns over such things as nitrous oxide emissions, triglycidal isocyanurate exposure effects, and disposal of used powder and wash line chemicals increase, so will the costs involved with keeping in compliance. To be sure, the pendulum swings both ways, and the day may come when liquid paint is equally attractive.

Change

In the good old days, all a company had to do was take a part, coat it with plastic, and send it to the customer. Business came from the company down the street, sales were done door to door, and all metal parts were fair game. Today, in the global market, fabrications, castings, and stampings are moving offshore to Asia and south to Mexico and Central America. The quality of finished product is improving through technological innovations in both materials and application methods. The challenge facing the powder-coating job shop is to not only find domestically produced products to finish, but also to offer foreign companies the value-added services needed to finish their products that have domestic demand. Today's powder coater must be able to not only compete in the finishing market, but assist the companies producing the parts to be coated in their fight to remain competitive.

The Internet has created a vast opportunity for those companies with the vision to exploit its power. It is now possible to create a relationship with a customer that may be hundreds of miles away, by offering finishing services to them en-route to their customers. A powder coater in Nevada can finish and package product for a customer in Mexico whose product is shipping to Seattle. A powder coater in New York can capture the business of a foundry in Ontario whose finished product is en-route to Florida. By using the Internet as a sales tool, no salesperson has to knock on their door, they only have to go online to find and develop this relationship.

Finally, no longer are metal parts the only parts that are suitable for powder coating. With the development of low-cure powders and visible-light-cured resins, wood products and plastic injection-molded parts are now being powder coated. These and other markets will be developed through the ingenuity and perseverance of the powder coating job shop as the desire and vision of the entrepreneurs who run them continue to explore the possibilities.

SUMMARY

The business world is an open book. Many of the chapters written will tell of successes and failures. No doubt, the powder-coating job shop will play an important role, and will be lucky to get a footnote at the bottom of the page. The mom-and-pop shops and the small coaters will rise and fall, and as the world grows smaller, the challenge to be successful will surely grow larger. But when the dust settles in the proverbial spray booth, the company whose product is the best seller will most likely have had it finished by a job-shop powder coater.

REFERENCE

Yahn, Greg. 2002. "21st Century Shops: Juggling Customers, Competitors, Compliance, and Change." Technical Paper FC02-106. Dearborn, MI: Society of Manufacturing Engineers.

Index

U

ultraviolet (UV) light, 22
urethane acrylic, 15-17, 24
utilities, 109

V

venturi operation—hoses and
    pumps, 141
vertical integration, 160-163
volatile organic compounds
    (VOC), 1-2, 4

W

waste disposal, 1
water and humidity, 124
water emissions, 1

Z

zinc, 53
zinc phosphatizing process, 136